The Fabric of Health

Dear reader:
The information in this book is
not intended as a replacement for
medical services, nor is it intended
as a substitute for any treatment
prescribed by your physician.

Credits:

Cover art:
Bioenergetic-art, by Henry F. Mende

Cover photography: Gary Ferrigno

Photograph of bunker on pg. 11:
©Don Gazzaway

Illustrations of sacred geometry:
© Fred Silva, www.lovely.clara.net

ISBN 0-9771555-0-1

THE FABRIC OF HEALTH

JOHN W. CARDANO

with PETER S. BARRY

Understanding Pain With Conscious Awareness

Acknowledgments

I am grateful to so many people who generously opened their hearts and minds to assist me in the evolution of this book over the last six years. Many of them appeared in my life just when I most needed the particular support or encouragement they could provide.

Nicole Cardano, as I share in the text, has been a wonderful influence on and participant in my journey these past 26 years. Ursula Flurer, a special person whose compassionate heart embraced this project and who provided unwavering support in bringing it to realization. Howard Eggers, who shared his brilliant ability for expanding my condensed thoughts into ideas that could be communicated.

So many have contributed their different blessings: Anne Simpkinson, Hob Calhoun, Sandy Clothier, Henry F. Mende, Theresa Cardano, Marilyn Cardano, John Fitzpatrick, Suzanne Berger, Betty Haynes, Skip Brach, Judith Brown, Peter Elliot, James E. Payne, Renette Saunders, Toby Martin, Mary Ann Weidner, Betsy Bess, Richard Grossinger, Barbara Kowalska, Don Ferrarone, and Reiner Lubge.

My deepest thanks to you all.

Contents

May our light align love and peace

I.

Introduction

Pain is an unpleasant part of life, experienced to some extent by everyone. Like many people, my life has been changed more than once by the intrusion of pain. Any type of pain can be inconvenient, but the experience of chronic pain can be truly debilitating.

When pain becomes a part of your everyday reality, it can reduce the scope of your life experience. Acting like a great contracting force, chronic pain can slowly crush your confidence, your pleasure, and your openness to the world around you. Meanwhile, life marches on, even if chronic pain overwhelms your ability to participate in it and appreciate it.

But pain has many faces, and as hard as it may be to reconcile, pain can also point the way to greater understanding of our selves and the further release of life's potential.

We rarely appreciate good health until it is lost, and while yearning for a return to normality, anxiety about health can grow. The theories on how health can be regained are legion, and determining the appropriate course of action can be difficult: Who is the best health advisor? What approaches and treatments can really work? Am I willing to do what it takes? How long might it last? Does my insurance cover it? Will I ever be the same again?

For many, health issues arise silently, over years, or the course of a lifetime. For me, everything changed in an instant: a healthy 22-year-old one moment, then, in a bright explosion of light, a seriously wounded soldier in Vietnam. My journey to rebuild my health has lasted more than 36 years and continues to this day. In fact rebuilding health for myself — not just physically, but emotionally, mentally, and spiritually — and others, has become my life's work. Not only has it been rewarding on a personal level, but I have also learned certain fundamentals that I believe can help anyone who suffers from constant pain or chronic health problems.

After my wounding in Vietnam, chronic physical pain was the overriding challenge of my recovery. I was told early on that there was "no hope" for curing the body-wracking signals that still emanated from my healed wounds. After countless examinations by numerous doctors the consensus was that I would never end the pain, though I perhaps could manage it through medication. That medical prescription meant a body, and a life, that became increasingly toxic. As many before me have experienced, this route not only masks the immediate issues without resolving them, it can lead to new problems that are equally serious, including depression and addiction.

Fortunately, we are blessed with self-awareness. Through awareness, and a sense of humor, life, even with pain, can be experienced as a great adventure. If we can realize that we are an actor in our own play, then we can understand that the role we choose and the actions we take every day can still determine the quality of our life and what happens in the final act. In other words, self-awareness, or more appropriately, conscious awareness, can help us overcome almost anything, even when we have been told that there is "no hope."

When I finally slowed myself down enough to be patient and consciously aware during the moments of my life, I began to understand that there are four elements of being – body, mind, emotion, and spirit. And I began to see that the process of living is a fabric that is woven by us each day and that establishes the blueprint for how we will handle the events of tomorrow. I have come to believe that conscious awareness is an essential element for anyone who wants to live a life of true health, not just physically, but mentally, emotionally, and spiritually as well.

For me it took years of confusion, agony, and medication before I was ready to change my circumstances. Pain and suffering supplied the immediate motivation, yet ultimately it was my deep desire to live life to its fullest. Once I was ready, having failed to find relief through traditional means, I made a personal commitment to live with conscious awareness. Through my journey, which has included much trial, error, and soul searching, I have been able to take responsibility for my health and, in so doing, every dimension of my life has improved.

Many people who are unhealthy, have emotional issues, or live with chronic pain turn to medication, relaxation techniques, or physical conditioning. While these are important elements, they aren't always enough. True healing begins at a higher level, where we can find release from tension, anger, stress, fear, and other disharmonious energies that create dysfunction in our bodies. By regaining patience and trust within ourselves, by opening up our heart to our own intuition, and by re-establishing self-love, we can open ourselves up to undreamed of potential and regain our health.

Through my research, study, and practice I have come to recognize that we are all bioenergetic beings — our life is a manifestation of the energies within us. Life as we know it incorporates a physical biology that is powered by emotional energy, mental ability, and spiritual consciousness. These four elements of the human experience weave together to express the moment-to-moment status of our being, making each of our lives an incredible art form. Consider how many times we have changed ourselves! Whenever we choose to use the power of our consciousness, we can and do change the quality of our energy, which then radiates out into our life. Sometimes the change might not be noticeable to anyone but our selves. Other times, people may comment on or celebrate the changes they see in us. Success can depend on a variety of factors, yet the most essential of these factors comes from our own conscious awareness.

Some changes can be as simple as doing something new, like practicing meditation or stretching. We can also learn to consciously break old patterns. Once we become excited about a new direction, it can affect how we move, think, and express our selves. Every new enhancement can bring about the desire for further change, just as exercise builds stamina, reshapes the contours of our body, and gives us a greater appreciation for our selves. Each change we make and live every day can affect how we feel and, therefore, how we are in life. The end result is that positive change can eventually inform every aspect of our being. We all have the potential to create ourselves anew - each of us is the greatest art form we will ever possess.

The Fabric of Health represents my understanding of how conscious awareness operates within the dimensions of body, mind, emotion, and spirit. Using conscious awareness can allow us to recover from chronic physical and emotional disabilities, while also helping to develop powerful, life-enhancing attributes that can remain important to us in our everyday lives.

More and more I see people whose health concerns are offered little or no hope of meaningful treatment by the medical establishment. Of course there are areas where traditional medicine has a solid track record. However, it is also true that there are many issues that are just not being addressed by today's health care systems. Today I am a teacher of bioenergetic art. In my work I seek to harmonize the energies and their flow throughout the entire being - physically, emotionally, mentally, and spiritually.

For anyone in physical pain, it is best to begin by consulting a doctor. Depending on many factors, the course of action to end pain and regain health may be quick or longer term. Supporting health in life is not necessarily a linear process. We are all lifelong students, learning to create true health and happiness in our own lives. Whatever course you choose, and whether your pain is physical, emotional, mental, or spiritual, I believe the integration of conscious awareness into healthy life practices is the path to regaining true health and, as importantly, to regaining your true self.

Through this book I hope to share the insights and experiences that have enhanced my ability to change from a life of chronic pain to living a life of health and happiness throughout the dimensions of my being. All of the events in this book are a part of my story.

=

2.
The Siege

Fire Support Base Sergeant, DMZ, April 1970. We were enjoying a few days of unusual quiet. I was hanging out with three other soldiers in a small, reinforced bunker. The bunker was dark, lit only by candles. Ribbed metal sheets supported the ceiling that was topped with four layers of sandbags to protect us.

A medic sat beside me on a bunk, another soldier sat on the floor, and a soldier named Tom stood three feet across from me talking about home. Without warning, a bright flash of light emerged above Tom's head. The ceiling blew open as a large mortar entered the bunker. As I sat there I watched as the mortar tore open Tom's chest and removed his entire groin area, then stop, sticking out of what had been his knee seconds before. The Chinese-made mortar didn't explode.

I helped the medic give aid to Tom in his last moments of life and then ran 20 or 30 yards through a hail of mortar fire to get back to my job as a linguist and cryptologist, intercepting and translating enemy communications.

That mortar was the first incoming round of a siege on the Support Base, located on the highest mountain-top in the Demilitarized Zone (DMZ) between North and South Vietnam. Officially the base didn't exist, as the DMZ was politically a no man's land, yet the high terrain had made the area an important strategic location in this war, as it had been for centuries before. There were two allied infantry companies and our four-man Radio Research unit on the hill. The camp was not far from the old French base at Dien Bien Phu.

Army intelligence put the number of regular North Vietnamese Army (NVA) troops surrounding our position at 5,000. Most days we numbered less than 180 men. At night, when the NVA owned the territory, I listened to the fluent Russian being spoken by helicopter pilots delivering supplies to the enemy.

During the moments that I wasn't focused on doing my job, I was gripped by strong emotions of terror, frustration, anger, worry, and disgust. There was, however, more than enough to do to distract me from such thoughts - it was common to work 14 to 22 hours per day for days or weeks at a time. There was satisfaction in staying current or even ahead of tasks, and being busy meant the heavy emotions couldn't weigh too much upon us. Not acknowledging the emotions, however, didn't mean they weren't having their effect.

Powerful emotions are forces that act both within our bodies and on those around us.

I was sent in to take over the communications intercept position from the Marines about five months earlier. The hill was an active duty station that was probed by regular enemy attacks. Already during my time with the Marines there had been a siege that lasted for more than a month. The area field infantry companies took turns defending the hill, but it was an unpopular and hazardous duty – when you hold a defensive position, you become a target. The infantrymen preferred field duty because it gave them more options on when and where to engage the enemy.

As different infantry companies came and went from the hill, I would brief their commanders on necessary information. The other men in my unit rarely interacted with anyone outside our small group. Yet the earlier siege had shown me the importance of having a working relationship with all the hill commanders. The Vietnamization of the war was a few months old and an elite South Vietnamese company (SVA) had been sent in to work with us and to prove their ability. This made for a unique composition of troops on the hill when the second siege began.

One commander was Army Captain Murk, a large man and a fierce soldier on his third tour of duty in Vietnam. He had been wounded on his first tour and had a metal plate put in his head from that action. He had refused two field promotions because he didn't want to leave the battlefield. He hated all "gooks," which created tension with the SVA unit we needed to coordinate with.

The SVA had already spent enough time on the hill for me to develop a working relationship with them, and my observations told me that they were effective fighters: the NVA often ran from them.

Captain Murk's group held the eastern half of the hill and our SVA allies held the western half; there was little communication between the two infantry companies. Life can be very complicated – though everyone on the hill shared the same goals, we were divided by language, culture, individual emotions, attitudes, and agendas.

My stay at the second siege lasted for 70 days. The NVA kept up a constant suppression fire on our position - one mortar round every 10 seconds, 24 hours a day, every day. The only break we had, if you could call it that, was during two weeks of evening ground assaults that involved everyone leaving the fortified bunkers for hand-to-hand combat.

Before and during the siege I made daily visits to the commanders in order to keep them informed and to evaluate their assessments of conditions. When I decided that the NVA's commitment of assets to take the mountain could overpower our response, I called the rear fire support base for artillery fire close in on our position.

Then one morning it was totally quiet. One member of my unit, Phil, also a linguist, and I decided that we could make the trip to a nearby section of our bunker that we hadn't dared visit since the siege began. It meant going out the door, making a 180-degree turn to the right along the outside wall, and going 12 feet. When we went, Phil was a step ahead of me. As we were just about to enter the bunker, he stopped to look at the nearby hill. A jet fighter was off-loading napalm, pulling out of its dive at tree-top level. That was the last thing I saw. Phil and I were blown through the bunker doorway by a mortar blast that landed eight feet behind us. After hearing thousands of rounds shriek down around us, I finally knew the answer to a question we always asked: You don't hear the one that gets you.

I regained consciousness on the ground. I felt like a pulsating orb – the pulsating was throughout my body, yet extended through the space that surrounded me. I saw Phil on the dirt floor beside me. He was moving. I felt a surge of frustration: the odds had finally caught up with me. I couldn't hear and I could barely see. It was difficult to move. The realization that I still had all my limbs gave me my first, slight sense of relief.

Intense conditions such as these can be psychologically traumatizing. The emotional intensity of the war, combined with the daily onslaught of scenes of horrific carnage, shattered many of my dearly held beliefs about human values. They also caused traumatic shock. These were regular ingredients of surviving on the hill. My physical injuries only added another dimension of pain to be overcome.

A person's ability to perform beyond normal physical limits is drawn from the human spirit, mental focus, and emotional power – all elements of the fabric of our being. It is these non-physical dimensions that can enable a traumatized soldier or a severely damaged body to keep moving forward to an intended goal.

Everyone on the hill pulled themselves through such events. It was a simple matter of survival and part of the responsibility each of us bore toward the other members of our group. Only when someone was literally destroyed outright, like Tom, did that responsibility end. If there was any potential to continue on, even for a short time, most did.

As everyone began to recover from the shelling of our bunker, the other soldiers opened a hole in the sand-bagged wall between the workspace and where we lay. I fought to remain conscious, knowing better than to fall into a coma from which I might never emerge. Phil and I were bleeding from head to toe and the concussion force of the explosion caused blood to seep out through my eyes and ears. A loud ringing filled my head, but I could somehow read lips. I saw us being reported as injured to our rear command and watched as a soldier mouthed the words: "Cardano won't make it."

The recognition of that statement pushed me to a new level of intention to survive. I had continuously made commitments to myself during the siege that I would not be killed.

Capt. Murk and a medic came charging into our bunker. Murk grabbed me by the collar, lifted me into the air and demanded to know if that was the first round of the day. We had formed a strong team and I recognized that he resented losing our working relationship. I nodded yes. He let go and I dropped back onto the floor. He charged out. The medic stayed behind and tended to us.

The burned wreckage of a Chinook helicopter that had been shot out of the air while delivering supplies sat on the landing pad. Because of the furious barrage of enemy mortar fire that came as a response to any helicopters approaching the hill, supplies would be dropped from so high up that they never landed inside the perimeter of the camp. I had no expectations that a medical evacuation could occur.

Amazingly, a few hours later, Capt. Murk appeared with three soldiers and announced that he had called in a medevac. He and another soldier grabbed my arms around their shoulders and out we went.

Whenever anyone was observed outside the bunkers, the heavy suppression mortar fire fell like rain. It is impossible at times to understand how anyone or anything could survive such fierce shelling, yet somehow we did. If I saw it in the movies, I would not believe it. Our bunker was on the northeastern side of the camp; Capt. Murk had to take us to the southwestern end for the medevac. The helicopter would have to land on the ammunition bunker.

As we made our way on the path between bunkers, South Vietnamese soldiers came out in tears to say farewell to me. At the sight of the Vietnamese, Capt. Murk became furious.

We arrived at the ammo bunker at the same moment as the South Vietnamese commander. He and a small group had also come to bid me farewell. Capt. Murk set me down, grabbed the other commander and threw him to the ground. The Vietnamese commander jumped back to his feet amidst an incredible hail of mortar fire. The two groups were facing each other down with M16s poised as others tossed Phil and me into the hovering helicopter. We flew off. It was only a few more months before our position on the hill fell to the NVA.

—

After 30 days spent in five medical facilities, I was back in the mountains of the DMZ. Even though my wounds had healed well enough, my body was still adjusting to the trauma of the event. Life just kept moving on; I felt I had to keep in step or suffer the system. If I had a problem, I told myself to "deal with it." I still had 10 weeks left on my tour of duty in Vietnam.

I could not deny the truth of my pain. Two medics had sewn up the series of wounds that extended from my ankles to the top of my neck on my backside. I had asked how many separate wounds had been sewn and their response was, "Don't know, we stopped counting in the high 20s."

My strong will to live pulled me through that life-threatening event and I felt lucky compared to so many others. I had no organ damage, nor did I lose any limbs. My main physical health issue was the extensive nerve damage I had sustained from the shrapnel. This caused severe muscle cramps, the intense sensation that areas of my body were being roasted in fire, and sharp bursts of pain as though an ice pick were continually stabbing into my legs. The effect was disorienting and, often, overwhelming.

The care given to my physical wounds was impressive, though it was immediately clear that my body didn't work the way it once had. Nerves had been severed and shrapnel that came to rest below the skin's surface was left inside for fear that digging in to get them would cause even more nerve damage. Pain-killing medication seemed the best alternative for my chronic pain.

The intercept and cryptology work that I had done back on the hill had been highly regarded and now I was getting the big compliment – more work. I had imagined that I would be sent back to the States, but when your organization knows that you can deliver what it wants, they keep you around. I kept myself going by shutting myself off from the pain. "Keep on moving," I said to myself, "live with it, and don't talk about it."

Once stationed back in the United States, I began my search for something that could relieve the constant pain. Each doctor said the same thing and I was given two basic options. The first was to get a "nerve clip," which meant that an operation would be performed to sever the nerve cord going into my leg. "What would that do?" I asked. "You would be able to stand in fire and not know it," the doctor responded. I found that option unacceptable.

The second option was to take more medication. My experience had already shown me that heavy medication was not an ideal solution, so I continued to make more appointments with more doctors in the hope of finding greater insight into my situation.

Then I received an appointment with a doctor at Walter Reed Army Medical Center, where the nation's top brass and even the President have been for treatment. This doctor was a colonel and a woman. A woman, I hoped, might be more sensitive to my plight.

As I entered her office she snarled at me, "You sniveling coward!" She stomped over to my x-ray that hung on a backlit wall. "These little pieces of metal wouldn't bother a real man." She kept up the barrage of insults for 40 minutes. Then she dismissed me.

Tender care, I assumed, was not her forte. I knew that a strong will could temporarily overcome some things in life, yet I also knew that I needed to deal with my reality, not mind fiction. I left Walter Reed feeling sorry for myself and feeling pity for the colonel.

Yet the colonel did have an effect on me. After that meeting I let go of any naive thoughts that someone else could take care of these problems for me. So I turned to medication as my only defense against the reality of the pain I was experiencing. I steeled myself to the future I faced: keep on moving, live with it, and don't talk about it.

—

I returned to the "world" from Vietnam in August, 1970. Within 24 hours I found myself walking along the streets of Boston. This city that I had enjoyed visiting so many times before now felt surreal to me. I was dressed in uniform and getting some hateful looks. My combat-developed instincts of self-protection were still on high alert.

It was a good feeling to land back in the States, yet it was also a deeply troubling time. I had been surprised at the difficulty of committing to coming home. Even though the news was censored in Vietnam, the ferocity of the anti-war sentiment was palpable. That, combined with the recognition of how much I had changed, gave me a sense of alienation. Who would want to hear about my life over there? And, if someone were interested, how could I describe it?

As I walked along the street, from the corner of my eye I noticed a black, filmy something that seemed to be clinging to my right upper arm. I snapped my arm out to the side to shake it off. It didn't move. I shook my arm again and spun around on high alert. With my full attention on it, I realized that a black vaporous cloud surrounded me, and it extended out at least three feet in all directions.

I didn't have a name for it at the time, but I instinctively knew that the dark energy field that engulfed me came from within. I instinctively sensed that I had been feeling its weight in many ways, a residue of all the death, fear, and trauma that I had been living.

After a few moments I came to a place of acceptance with this energy field and moved on. That was my first recognition of an aura. From that day in Boston, until many years later, I don't recall any other experiences of my energy body. I suspect there were some, but my vigorous use of medication erased all memory of them.

—

By 1974 I had graduated from the University of Massachusetts, gotten married, and moved to Maine. It was four years after Vietnam and I was on my honeymoon. One evening my wife, Gloria, had gone to bed while I sat and enjoyed watching the evening light play over the harbor below our rental cottage. As it grew dark outside, I became very uncomfortable and filled with fear.

When I lived in the DMZ, any light or shadow that suggested the silhouette of a person became a target to be destroyed. Though I realized that I was now safely situated, that realization had no effect on my sense of dread and mortal danger. As I sat there I tried to resolve my wartime conditioning with my current truth. Sweat poured from my body. I felt confused about how to cope with the different traumas that coexisted within me. Weary in the darkness, I sought the warm comfort of my wife and the oblivion of sleep. When I awoke, my fears had receded and my focus returned to getting through each day.

The mind has a strong instinct for survival. It remembers and can automatically initiate any conditioned reaction that has proved useful in the past. The sound of a helicopter's rotor blades sent me diving for cover in Vietnam, and I still felt the same urge when I was safely back in the States. In the same way, survival strategies learned as a child or teenager can continue to be automatically applied to our daily life as an adult, even when their effectiveness has long passed. Worse, we tend not to be aware that this is happening. Becoming aware of these conditioned reactions is required before we can learn new, more appropriate responses for the truth of our present lives.

While in Vietnam, we all created an emotional defense system that allowed us to keep going. After a brutal event like Tom's death, we referred to it as "good training." That perspective gave us a high level of emotional detachment. It was effective, but the emotional rebound that came years later still needed to be dealt with. Such emotional discomfort became layered in with the associated physical and mental trauma. The physical aspect was obvious, but the other dimensions proved more difficult to recognize, and were even harder to accept. All dimensions of my trauma contributed to the pain I felt.

Over time I became apprehensive about my pain. I began to fear it. I was angry at feeling helpless and unable to take care of my situation. My emotions knotted up inside me. During the experience of tremendous amounts of pain, whether physical or emotional, there isn't much we won't do to escape it.

When I was in its throes, it was difficult to behave in the way that I wanted, and in a way that I could respect. When you are willing to do almost anything to escape from pain, you can no longer trust the motivations behind your actions. This leads to deeper distrust of your self on a spiritual level.

Over the next several years, my pain continued to increase. This included a sharp stabbing sensation running through my body from head to toe, as well an intense discomfort and burning. My doctors experimented with different medications. The drug with the least side effects was Tylenol #4, each pill containing a grain of codeine. With medication, the worst of the pain would subside enough to enable me to pay attention to other aspects of my life. But the pain never really vanished and uncomfortable side effects such as an anxious restlessness and an upset stomach became the norm. I came to understand these side effects as an expression of a wider disruption in my health. Not only were other bodily systems being interfered with but the toxic buildup had its own effects. Outside of food intake, my daily diet became 10 Tylenol #4s, a fifth of some type of alcohol, a 6-pack of beer or some wine, and grass. There were no vitamins, minerals, or herbs in this regimen.

I learned to live and function in this state of pain and medication; it became my status quo. I also knew that the more I identified with being a wounded person, the deeper I sank into forever being wounded.

I continued my search for better options through doctors, counselors, friends, and elders, and still I found no way to soothe the pain that engulfed me.

=

3.
Child/Teacher

The fire in the wood stove was mesmerizing. Yellow, blue, and violet flames danced in a primal rhythm of combustion. There was a soothing comfort to the movement of light.

I was floating with my thoughts, trying to relax from the efforts of the day. My body was letting tension release where knots had gathered in my muscles and in my attitude.

Nicole, my 2-year-old daughter, was playing with her toys. She walked over to a piece of wood that I had left lying on the floor next to the stove. As she picked it up, I ordered her to stop. Nicole put the wood down and looked at me. "Why?" she asked, and something inside me clicked.

In an instant, I realized that I was needlessly controlling her actions, and it was due to unresolved emotions within me. She had asked a simple question and I was exposed. That single moment opened me up to a new understanding of communication and relationship.

"Good question," I said. "Thank you. Go right ahead with what you were doing." I realized and accepted how much she could teach me. The purity of action in children is a lesson for us all. Of course, the teaching relationship flows back and forth between us, but a child's innocence can refresh an adult's view of the world. I became aware that my ongoing emotional state was inappropriate to the present moment I was experiencing.

Emotional tension affects every aspect of our being. Emotion communicates how we feel about what is happening in a given moment. Gaining conscious awareness of our emotional states allows us to better understand why we say and do certain things. When my emotional state is based on something that has happened in my past, I am not being true to the present moment. Such stress need not always be based in the past; it can also be a byproduct of expectations about the future. I suddenly understood that gaining a conscious awareness of my current emotional state was crucial to having a healthy presence in life.

Nicole's question pointed out to me the emotional tension I was feeling, which had caused me to be too forceful in that moment. I knew that if I brought patience and peaceful emotions to a given moment, I could create a pleasant, open basis for mutual interaction. If I am emotionally wrought with anger, fear, anxiety or worry, those feelings become the basis for my motivations, reactions, and relationships with others. If I am aware of how I am feeling now, I am more able to be responsive and flow naturally with the present moment. I am able to better deal with life as it is, rather than react from places of unresolved emotion about how it was or how it might yet be.

Nicole's question was her natural emotional response — honest curiosity based on her present moment. She was merely picking something up in her play area, and neither the hot wood stove nor her holding the wood itself was the issue. Everything was safe. I had snapped at Nicole out of my own emotional tension. My daughter was perfectly clear about how she felt, and her curiosity gave me clarity about my actions. This realization allowed me to change my emotional posture. As a result, our communication flowed more comfortably. That lesson was a wonderful gift.

With this insight, we began to communicate in a way that respected the other person's participation. If either of us had ignored the other, a tension could have developed between us. A small tension, perhaps, yet any tension sets a foundation for behavior that is reactive rather than responsive. An unconscious

reaction maintains or even increases the tension of
a situation. A conscious response sends a clear message of how we are feeling as we participate. The intent
is to be clear regarding the issue, and to be free from
emotional tension.

My convalescence as a wounded person living with
chronic pain only began to become effective when
I recognized that I had to resolve my pain on every
dimension – physical, mental, emotional and spiritual.

=

4.

A Call to Awareness

After years of living a life limited by pain, medication, and a false belief that nothing could change my state of being, I came to view my health issues as a call to awareness. Pain is a message from within, telling me that something is wrong. My pain and I are best served if I communicate, with myself and with others, in a clear and responsible manner. Being overly emotional or acting like a wild beast about my pain is not productive. Emotional balance - even some emotional detachment — is required in order to achieve a sense of self. I knew it was time for personal change.

Though the seeds of change had been growing in me for some time, it was my divorce that proved to be the last straw. It forced me to renew my search for relief. Both the war and my divorce destroyed the naive beliefs and illusions that I held about how my life would play out. Marriage, I had expected, would be lifelong. My divorce caused emotional pain in me that rivaled the agony of my physical pain.

For my wife and I, communication had never been honest enough. Trying to make things work without clearing up the root issues took its toll. I looked into a mirror only to see a haggard, aging man tormented by disillusion with the events and relationships in his life.

I had reached the limits of my misery. Misery filled all the dimensions of my being: the physical pain and disability; the emotional currents of anger, fear, worry, loneliness, and anxiety; the mental images of death and war; and my soul crying out for fulfillment. It had been building for years. I came to understand that only by searching within myself would I ever regain my health. The best road out from the dark place I inhabited was to take personal responsibility for my health and for my life.

It was 13 years after my wounding on the hill before I began to see this as my path to becoming the person I knew myself to be. I hadn't created all the situations I had been through, and the past couldn't be changed. How I viewed the past, interpreted it, and responded because of it – those things I could change. Years of frustration and self-reflection led me to realize that I could choose how I wanted to live my experiences. I made a total commitment to become the person I wanted to be and to honor my intuition.

Taking personal responsibility opened up my life far beyond what I could have imagined. I gave up the medication and cut back on drinking. I chose to give up activities that I loved, like scuba diving and tennis.

Those sports had allowed me to feel that I hadn't lost my physical participation in the world, yet they also brought on periods of excessive pain and, subsequently, heavy medication. Instead, I found new, positive ways to engage myself.

In 1982 acupressure had been introduced to me through a friend who was studying it at that time. Armed with enough information, I was able to start doing acupressure work on myself. I spent the next several months living like a human pretzel as I held my hands on various combinations of energy points located all over my body. For example, I would hold my right index finger against an acupoint between my shoulder blades, while I placed my left index finger against an anklebone. The result was true pain relief for the first time. It was thrilling to attain even small periods of feeling pain-free.

That experience inspired me to immerse myself in other non-traditional ways of healing. I took trips to study a variety of holistic health practices, or modalities. The study of massage enabled me to feel comfortable holding, rubbing, and working my physical body. Polarity work — the study of how energy moves through us - reinforced and expanded my knowledge of how to integrate enhanced energy flow in the body. The study of reflexology taught me the powerful effect that releasing tension in the feet has on different selected areas of the body. Cranial sacral – the energy balancing of the brain and spine – deepened my sensitivity to subtle energy pulses and expanded my awareness of the intricate delicacy of the central nervous system. Reiki and Omega Shakti – the studies of focusing and enhancing life force – expanded and developed my potential to channel energy in support of healing.

Though I threw myself into these studies, change was difficult. I understood their value, but I found it equally important for me to consciously acknowledge that value in order to fully accept it. All of the "medical experts" and resources that I had sought out had declared my situation to be impossible to change. I had to trust myself. It was scary. Yet even in complicated conditions I have learned that if I am present or fully conscious to an event, in that moment a decision will become clear.

Being fully present to events as they occur is living in the moment. Our attention is best placed on what is happening now. If we give full attention to what is current and act in accordance with whom we intend to be, if we respond rather than react, the future will truly take care of itself. It requires preparation and commitment to change from being anxious about the past and future to being at peace with them.

For years I traveled, studying new modalities and returning home to practice on myself until I had them mastered. The process was gradual and rewarding. I met others on the path of understanding how body, mind, emotion and spirit form us. It was empowering to be part of a community of seekers. My health improved and my self-esteem grew.

Additionally, I began studying Taoism, Hinduism, Ayurveda (the Indian science of life), Native American spirituality, the Mayans (for their cultural and spiritual insights), quantum physics, sacred geometry (understanding the symbols that populate our universe), and even the Superstring theory of our universe — anything that contributed to my insights into a deeper understanding of life and health.

I found that what all these modalities had in common was a fundamental belief in the vibrational energy that informs all things. Interest in vibrational energy work as a modality of health attracted me from the beginning, and I was excited by the success I had experienced by working on myself with acupressure. When we commit ourselves to learning something new, unexpected understanding may come to us.

At first I would place my fingers on particular acupoints. With comfort and familiarity, I let things flow. Soon I was holding the acupoints with my fingers away from my body and achieving equal or greater success. The more I opened myself to the flow of energy, the more powerful the work became.

I was even able to make positive connections to my experiences back on the hill in Vietnam. There, the insight of an appropriate course of action came to me when I allowed myself to let go and get into the flow of the work, intercepting messages or going out into all the crazy scenes during the siege. We are connected to the fullness of our being and the universe around us by vibrational energy, and it empowers us to understand more about how everything is linked together.

In 1988, I moved down the coast of Maine from Mt. Desert Island to Portland though I regularly returned to spend time with my daughter.

On one fall visit, I went into Bar Harbor for breakfast. As I enjoyed my meal, I felt an intuition to go buy a book. What book, I didn't know, but I had become used to receiving intuitive guidance from the spiritual world and increasingly found that if I listened to this intuition it would bring benefits to my life and my journey. I came to enjoy and appreciate this intuition as a signal to pay attention to what was inside of me. If I didn't resist it or ignore it, my life could be enhanced by it.

This time, however, I was not open to it. I had my agenda and I didn't want to make any changes. I stubbornly held to my original plan, resisting my impulse and re-establishing through my internal monologue that I was there to spend the weekend with my daughter and that was that. But the guidance became stronger, more insistent. Still I held my intention: "No, I am not going for a book, thank you." After I had driven out of town, the issue was forgotten.

The next morning I was again enjoying a breakfast in town. And once again my inner guidance pushed me to go get a book. I continued to reassert myself. "No, thank you. I am here for a visit with my daughter."

Well, this book was not to be denied – I found I could no longer enjoy my meal. Then the insistence moved to a level I had not experienced before or since. My whole being filled with a sense that if I didn't get a book, and I still had no idea what book I was to get, utter doom was going to be my fate. This intense premonition was enough to get me to loosen up and listen.

Soon I was walking down the street. I found a store, Eden Rising, which carried products from the Far East and featured spiritual and holistic books. The books were all the way in the back, obscured by other displays. As soon as I entered the store a book at the far end of the room caught my eye. It was surrounded by numerous other books, but still quite obvious to me. There was no question: it was the only book that was shining with a radiant glow.

I walked back, grabbed a copy without looking too much at it, and spun around to make my purchase. I left the store and shared another great day with my daughter.

That book was *The Cosmic Octave*, by Hans Cousto. It was a tiny little book that became instrumental in expanding my understanding of vibrational frequencies and introduced me to the use of tuning forks in healing. Cousto explains how vibrational frequencies are associated with everything that exists. These frequencies can be measured and understood mathematically, by using the concept of the octave from music. In fact our senses pick up these vibrations and translate them into our experiences of movement, sound, and color. Cousto utilizes a specific set of tuning forks that have been designed to resonate with the known frequencies emitted by the planets. He relates how ancient systems recognized the fundamental mathematical relationship between particular planets and particular organs based on their vibrational frequencies. By holding a related tuning fork on or above a pain location in the body, pain release can be brought to that area.

I often mentioned this book to others and eventually gave away a number of copies in order to stimulate conversation. Yet no one else found the value in it that I did. Our lives are all so different. My intuition was right in selecting it for me at that point in my life.

A path of events opened up for me from my reading. In subtle ways there have been a wide variety of connections and friendships that have developed because of that little book. Following my inner guidance that day, even if reluctantly, opened me to change, and change can bring many unexpected gifts.

=

Transforming

The seasons of life
Change as I
Practice in patience
Release expectations
Accept each moment
Filter my reality
Refine my alignment
With personal truth

What colors
Will this butterfly be

Each thought
Each word
Each intention
Aligns my potential

My breath
Steadies and stretches
My incubating character

Oh divine guidance
Imbue brilliant light
Throughout the world
Infuse me
With light and bliss

5.
A Fabric

It was mid-April. The moon was almost full and the water temperature at the foot of the dam was 48 degrees. The conditions were set for the elver run to begin. Elvers, baby eels, make their run upstream from the salty ocean waters where they were born when the moon and tide are just right. I spied a seal nearby, ready for a spring delicacy. The high tide would come at dusk.

I prepared my fishing equipment, and myself, so that I was ready. Once done, patience was the key.

I sat in the cool night air as the tide came in and sensed that spring was coming to the harbor. I've always loved being intimately involved with the details of nature and, more important, I needed such experiences as part of my journey to health.

The eel, at any stage of its life, had widely been considered a nuisance in Maine. There had always been an abundance of other delicious fish and preferences for haddock, trout, crab, and lobster were common. Eels are slimy fighting fish that can be difficult to deal with. Nocturnal creatures, they become active in the evening. Fishermen using rod and reel at dusk would commonly catch an eel instead of their intended prey.

Once caught, they would have to deal with the slimy, strong smelling, thrashing eel, which often would try to wrap itself around an arm. Most fishermen would simply cut their line as soon as they recognized that an eel was on their hook. If the eel were taken home, the easiest thing to do would be to throw it in the freezer. Even after thawing, once an eel was cut up and tossed in a frying pan, it often created great commotion as the powerful nerves in this primordial fish would cause the eel pieces to jump all over the place. "Those blasted eels don't ever die!" Often the missus would forbid eels in the home.

In other areas of the world, particularly in Asia, at all stages of its life the eel is considered a delicacy. Those outlets became so demanding that a high priced elver market came to exist in the rural coast of Maine. In fact, people began thrashing about in every stream and waterway along the eastern seaboard from Florida to Canada.

I had the pleasure of experiencing both elvers and eels as gourmet delights in Japan. After military service, I returned to college to study the Japanese language and culture. A summer of living with a Japanese family in 1974 gave me an appreciation for the finer attributes of eels. I toured the eel growing ponds in Shizuoka, Japan. And after I had lived in Maine for a while, I began researching and fishing eels locally.

During the spring elver season, paths leading to potential good fishing spots had now become processions of lights weaving through the dark, as folk would fish elbow to elbow. This is an interesting example of how different circumstances in life can cause people to open up to something new or different — to change their behavior. The economic opportunity offered by eeling had given a great many people an incentive to change the way they thought and acted. While more subtle quality-of-life improvements are generally not as strong an incentive as money in bringing about changes in attitude, the principle is the same. Making change requires an appropriate level of belief in the potential benefits that can be attained in the future.

Elver fishing required getting permission from landowners to commercially fish their property. A couple I knew, Bob and Barbara, owned the land I frequented and we shared many wonderful conversations. We enjoyed talking about how so many things, including nature, were similar to an exquisite tapestry in which all the elements are like individual threads, where each thread has its own role to play in adding to the fullness of the fabric.

One day Barbara showed me a picture of an area she really loved. "Can you imagine this picture would convey so much if even one thing were removed?" she asked. The picture showed a mature stand of mixed trees and shrubs. A stream meandered down the hillside and flowed into a cove. Each element had a presence that blended in perfect proportion to the others. It seemed that indeed nature had woven a tapestry that was calm and soothing, yet in the same instant conveyed the energetic vitality of each element and captured the awe inspiring power of nature.

I came to appreciate that health is also a fabric. A very delicate and mysterious fabric where the threads of body, mind, emotion and spirit each contribute to our experience of life. We are spiritual beings involved in a physical adventure, with a mental ability and an emotional power system. The central challenge of the adventure is to evolve in a way that keeps the entire fabric in harmonious flow.

Increasingly, through my studies and practices, I felt the flow of energy from one element in the fabric of health move through to the others. I was on a path of learning to be responsive to the subtle messages of the other three threads – intuitive input, emotional moods, and mental attitudes. Up to this point in my life, I had been responding mostly to my physical symptoms - aches and pains do get your attention!

The body is far more than a vehicle for getting us around. It is our presence in the material world, a presence that allows us to experience and express how we feel and think. The dimensions of our fabric of health together compose the full range of vibrations that make up our being. The body itself can be described as having a very slow vibration, and individual organs also each have their own unique vibrational expression. Our five senses allow us to perceive and understand the things that happen around us at faster, or higher, vibrations, like light, color, and sound. Our senses are our antennas on the world, picking up the subtle vibrations that surround us.

We all have the experience of using an antenna to tune in a radio or television broadcast by picking up specific vibrational waves. The ear, for example, receives and translates waves of sound. The eye converts light waves into meaningful images. The mouth both translates flavors and focuses the vibrations of our vocal cords. Our most sophisticated modern equipment can monitor these vibrational energies, but no one fully understands how any of these senses integrate life together. The experience of these vibrations is life. Eat something, touch someone, enjoy a favorite piece of art — these are all vibrational patterns that we understand and enjoy and that can have an emotional effect on us.

If you have an MRI, an EKG, or any of a wide variety of physical tests, each one records, and is a reflection of, the vibrational condition of your being at that moment. Similar to the sound of a great orchestra, each person is the total sum of many vibrations that together weave the fabric of health.

Learning to be aware of and appreciate as many of these vibrations as possible is an art. It is the art of conscious living. Developing this consciousness is a subtle matter. The qualities that are demanded are sensitivity and quiet. It is very different from the hustle and drama of modern life. As consciousness grows, however, the quality and enjoyment of life also grows. By becoming sensitive to the reasons for my tension and chronic pain, and being more aware of their vibrational presence, I become better able to release them from my body. In this way I can smoothly integrate conscious awareness into a full and busy life.

=

6.
An Energy Being

When I began working on myself with acupressure, I became more aware of my energy body, and of the state of my vibrational health. By working with the body's meridians, the pathways of energy for the organs and other body parts, I was able to open energy flow that had been congested and impeded. As I held acupoints, I could feel the energy flowing along the invisible energy pathways. Long-held tensions began to be released.

A few times during my marathon acupressure sessions, which could last for days, I found myself observing the sessions from outside my body. Such out-of-body experiences were initially bewildering. The ability to feel energy moving through me, and of being out of body, while still being totally at one with myself, was a profound experience. During one particularly joyous event, I was able to observe myself from a branch outside the window, a branch I shared with two chickadees. I felt myself sitting between them in a space no bigger than the space they occupied. As I continued to focus on myself in this experience, one chickadee became uncomfortable and flew off. A few moments later the other also seemed to notice my presence and took flight. I sensed that the birds were able to accept me while I remained in spiritual stillness, but not when I expanded the self-recognizing part of my ego. Other similar events have happened with birds and other animals when I entered my consciousness and held it in an open, expansive awareness but without any inclusion of my ego. When I focused attention on my participation with the animals, the connection would be broken.

I finally became able to achieve prolonged periods during which I did not feel pain for the first time in many years. This opened me to a powerful new respect for the energy in and around my body. I again had experiences of my aura, but it was no longer the black cloud that had surrounded me that day in Boston years ago. Now my aura felt clear, expansive, and uplifting.

My experience with the chickadees showed me how truly connected we are to everything. The modern physics theory of non-locality supports this idea: the theory reveals that a molecule on one side of the universe can be affected by what happens to a molecule on the other. When I stub my toe and say "ouch," the connection between the toe and throat is vibrational energy. It seems as though my mind is home to my consciousness, yet the mind is not consciousness. Consciousness is throughout my being.

When the pain would settle back in, my outlook on the world would dim considerably. The experiences of pain relief, however, gave me faith in my potential to heal. I continued to work on myself and to study more modalities. Throughout this process I practiced Chinese Taoist meditations on the Inner Smile (smiling into all parts of the body), the Microcosmic Circuit (an energetic orbit of energy flow in the body) and the Six Healing Sounds (integrating sounds, movement, and emotions related to specific organs). Years passed as I did these meditations once or twice each day. The new modalities allowed me additional release from my inner tensions and greater understanding of how energy flows through us and creates us.

Ancient Chinese medicine, Native American wisdom, and Ayurvedic medicine (the ancient medicine of India) are a few of the sources for appreciating how we are integrated into the flow of all that exists.

If we open our imagination, we can see that everything is composed of a primary essence. This essence has been given many names: chi, prana, ki, wakan and electromagnetic energy.

In the fullness of the universe, chi is spiritual essence. It is beyond the definition of words. The ancient sages were profound when they spoke of it as indescribable, eternal, and infinite. Only when this spiritual essence enters the dimensions that we experience does it become describable.

Chi has a spiritual quality. Spiritual essence, as it exists in this physical dimension, has recognized virtues such as trust, fairness, calmness, patience, courage, forgiveness, and gentleness. These spiritual virtues exert a positive vibrational force in us that can motivate us to positive actions.

In the moment that a child is conceived, spiritual alignment occurs. Light essence from the universe above and the earth below unite to form a central channel of light energy that is essential to life. This light energy empowers the growth of the child. During the early stages of growth, earth energy predominates. The earth energy grounds us, guides us, and supports the physical growth of the body. Over the span of life, the qualities of the light energy and the earth essence blend in different proportions as we complete physical growth and intentionally pursue intellectual efforts.

As the body develops, the organs act as the portals between the spiritual, physical, and emotional dimensions. Universal spiritual energy is refined and defined by each organ, and each organ has become associated with particular virtues.

Our perception may tell us that our body is a solid, but atomic physics has shown that we are 99.9% space. There is a lot going on in all that space — it is the home to energy flow and consciousness!

Energy centers, or chakras, are major energy flows that integrate with the central channel. Chakra is a Hindu word for an energy vortex within our energy system. There are seven major chakras.

The root chakra is the earth connection and also the earth opening of the central channel. It is located at the base of our trunk (between the legs). When we marvel at the amount of energy that young people have, that abundant energy is a demonstration of a root chakra that has its original integrity. Children flow with nature.

The crown chakra is the opening at the top of the head; it functions within the flow of the central channel, which continues far above the body.

The remaining five chakras spiral out of the front of the body on the midline of the central channel and each has a corresponding vortex of energy at the back of the body. In an advanced state of energy clarity, the chakras are a disc of energetic vibrational light expanding out in all directions. Moving up from the root chakra along the central channel, the major chakras are: sex chakra – located just above the pubic bone; solar plexus chakra – located in the upper abdomen where the floating ribs are; heart chakra – located up from the base of the sternum (measure using the width of your index and middle fingers, there is a little indent there); throat chakra – located just above the collar bone; third eye chakra – just above the central line of the eyebrows. The energy body is a dynamic field, so these locations are approximate. Expansion and contraction of these areas occurs in various locations at various times. Therefore, a particular energy center is not confined to a particular spot like a dot on a map. Each chakra is recognized for its relationships with particular emotions, physical aspects, and qualities of being.

There are major, minor and mini chakras. The major chakras are the energy centers along the central channel mentioned above. Minor chakras relate to specific organs, glands, and the palms of the hands and the soles of the feet. Mini chakras are the numerous acupoints of the meridian system. Chinese medicine is based on acupoints and Western science has verified their existence. The proof is recent but the discovery ancient by sages who used patience and gentleness to open up to some of nature's secrets.

Similarly, those working in the field of modern science today require patience. Within the scientific community, formulas exist that provide incredible accuracy to describe our world, even though the concepts that generate them are beyond the present ability of science to validate. Superstring theory puts forth the supposition that at the core of life there are infinitesimally small pieces of "string" that vibrate. It is the vibrational pattern of these strings that determines what things are. Vibrational resonance determines and identifies everything in the material world, a plant, a chair, a painting, or a person. Superstring theory appears to have the capacity to answer all the questions of science, yet the tools to prove the theory do not exist.

As science gets closer to believing that a "theory of everything" has been found, the teachings of ancient sages and mystics appear more profound than ever. The fundamental point is that everything is a vibra-

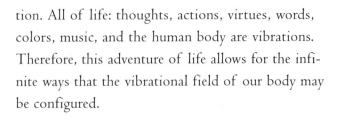

tion. All of life: thoughts, actions, virtues, words, colors, music, and the human body are vibrations. Therefore, this adventure of life allows for the infinite ways that the vibrational field of our body may be configured.

The aura is another major dynamic in the human energy system. The auric field begins at the edge of the body and extends outward with seven layers. Generally, stretching the arms out to the side demonstrates the extent of the auric field. It is shaped in the form of an egg with the fuller end above the head.

The body has both physical and etheric parts. Within the etheric parts, and overlaid with it, are various geometric patterns that enhance and focus the quality of resonant fields.

Sacred geometry relates that there are geometric shapes throughout life that are essential to a high quality of development. The spiral at the end of a seashell is the same spiral form seen in a satellite's picture of a hurricane, or a galaxy. Sacred geometry facilitates understanding such relationships. It is not possible to separate out, other than for the sake of discussion, the interwoven, symbiotic, interdependent threads of the fabric of life. Like being in nature, all of the experience is, there are no parts. Life is a holistic experience.

Understanding life is accomplished by observing it from different angles, inspecting its various parts. However, the observations and parts do not equal the whole. It is this fact that brings each person to awareness of the need to experience personal satisfaction in his or her relationship with themselves and in their actions in life.

Thus the individual way that energy moves through the threads of the fabric is always unique. My attitudes, physical body, mental consciousness, emotional needs and responses are unique - the same can be said for everyone throughout time. Additionally, this is true for all the stages of growth in this life. I would love to have had the understanding and composure that I feel now when I was younger!

Therefore, the status of our health is a personal bioenergetic message. The spleen, for instance, is an organ that filters and stores blood and produces white blood cells for the immune system. In the emotional dimension, the spleen is a vibrational energy field. The spleen is in a harmonious state when I am relating to my self in a fair, open manner, and I am connected to the world as a centered and grounded person. If, however, I am filled with worry and self-doubt, this state of emotional disharmony can have its base in the physical organ and be reflected in the spleen's energy field. Emotional disharmony creates a contractive vibrational state that tangles and eventually creates knots in the energy field, gradually affecting the physical health of the body.

Since everything is in continuous connection and flow, this disharmonious condition permeates the entire being. Some energy backs up, some energy stagnates, and other energy heats up or may seem to disappear. Fears that establish themselves in youth may not manifest as a specific physical condition for 15 or even 60 years. Yet during the span of life, the health issues that arise will have some connection to this ongoing internal disharmony.

For me, fears established early in life began constricting the quality of energy flowing to my kidneys, which then stunted the quality of energy flow to my liver and other organs. I was never consciously aware of this disharmony. Now, however, I am more aware of the health and emotional consequences that such disharmony can cause in my body, and I have been endeavoring to expand my energy flows ever since I assumed personal responsibility for my health.

Understanding the relationships between various health issues, or the issue behind a particular condition, requires patience. The fabric of health contains tremendous amounts of information. This information can be accessed through patience and conscious awareness.

As the lungs draw in fresh air and exhale CO_2, there is also an exchange of fresh chi for tired chi. The chakras are also generating a healthy exchange of energy. It is desirable for the entire body to constantly be in a healthful exchange. It is necessary to take in food and eliminate waste in a regular way, to grow new cells and slough off old cells. The process is repeated throughout our being. Change and renewal is the natural pattern.

The robust nature and physical beauty of youth express a vibrational harmony of being. As the young evolve, the radiance of their health signals the quality of nature's energy within them. The process of maturing is a life-long adventure filled with challenges from societal forces and external events as well as from internal personal choices.

There are numerous stages of youth during which opportunities for assessment occur - changing schools, dating, sport's activities, choosing a profession, or observing death. These assessment times are critical: this is when decisions are made regarding how we will live our lives. Do I honor what I know and feel is my truth, or do I not? It is our greatest challenge.

The resources for continuing to build a healthy body truly draw from all the threads of the fabric. Proper nutrition, a balance of exercise and rest, a mental attitude that respects the self, a balanced emotional state, and a spiritual awareness about what is important to one's self can all have a huge impact on how our lives unfold.

As the body develops during the miracle of birth and growth, a multi-dimensional being emerges with all its integrated fields. The chakras collect, manage, and transform various vibrational tones, or frequencies, of energy. The lower chakras step up and harmonize raw energy, as well as integrate it into circuit patterns in the chakras for specific energy use.

Simultaneously, the auric field coordinates the energy flow of the chakras as it integrates vibrational patterns into aspects of the physical body. The body allows the immediate experience of life. While the energies of the chakras affect what the body is becoming, the auric field reflects the underlying vibrational blueprint. Both the energies of the chakras and the aura's blueprint can be greatly affected by personal beliefs, attitudes, intentions, and all mental and emotional patterns.

As in "real" life, the blueprint is not always followed. There may be disruptive forces that inhibit, say, a particular organ, and a life turns out differently from the blueprint plan.

An ill state of health is reflected in the body, in the chakras, and in the auric field. During illness or injury, the healthy flow of energy becomes disrupted throughout the entire being. Various types of stress and tension can have long-term effects - some serious, others less so. It is the balancing of tension and goals that makes life a great adventure.

The ramifications of emotional and physical events are present in our bodies every day. In my life, being in the intensity of Vietnam sent me on a completely different

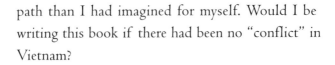

path than I had imagined for myself. Would I be writing this book if there had been no "conflict" in Vietnam?

It is a fundamental truth of life that chi is the ultimate substance of everything: humans, animals, stone, air – everything. Chi, being a substance of phenomenal variety, is mutable within the nature of the thing that it composes and it expresses the various qualities of that thing. As chi expresses spiritual principal, it is light – brilliant, expansive, harmonizing light in all variety of clear colors.

The merging of the physical and etheric body is not readily perceivable. Look at a plant in the yard. Even though we may experience the emotional calming effect of plants, sunlight and plant is all that is visible. Just as we are right now surrounded by invisible radio and light waves, we are also surrounded by other vibrational frequencies that are outside of our perception.

The intricacy of this vibrational layering that the dimensions maintain throughout our being is amazing. In the embryo, parallel pathways of energetic flow develop. Foundational energy from the developing kidneys generates the spine, which also becomes a channel for light energy that complements the quality of the central nervous system.

Health issues can be addressed from all locations within the fabric of health. Each health issue is mirrored in the energy system that composes our being. All of me participates in forming my total consciousness.

Taking this kind of comprehensive approach to healing can yield dramatic results. The deeper in the body that a health issue occurs, the more intense the experience can be. Personal adjustment may be required as change is brought to current circumstances in life.

When I meet with a client, I prefer to have an initial period of discussion regarding why we are meeting. Discovering what a particular physical ailment represents on an emotional level often brings recognition that the person acted in a way that violated their harmonic state (for example: feeling pressured by family or friends to behave in a way that emotionally didn't feel "right"). Through this process, consciousness is opened. Consciousness is the strongest force we have in guiding the energetic power that affects our healthy growth. Attention and intention are important in focusing energy. Our bodies slowly become an expres-

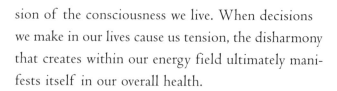

sion of the consciousness we live. When decisions we make in our lives cause us tension, the disharmony that creates within our energy field ultimately manifests itself in our overall health.

Once the emotional elements are brought out, I can have a session where the client can relax and I am able to release tensions and empower energetic flow throughout the body, chakras, and the auric fields. The harmonizing effect empowers the client to live their personal truth with a renewed sense of ease, and re-establishes greater harmonious flow throughout their being.

One client came to me wondering if I could help a weakened heart. A heart attack had damaged the "tip" of the heart and they had been told that nothing could be done: "You can live with this condition," the doctors said. All I knew was that the presenting issue was a weakened heart. But I could sense immediately that the person's energy level was low and that they felt a profound timidity, or fear, in living their life. During the energy work, I noticed that a number of areas in the organs, chakras, and aura had also become weak. In addition to the heart, the spleen, kidneys, liver and pericardium all held tension. The energy flow was disharmonious. After a couple of sessions, the energy flows had been cleared, strengthened, and harmonized. The client looked and felt better. By coincidence, the client was soon asked to take an echo stress test by a cardiologist. Much to their surprise, the heart tested as being perfectly healthy.

So we see that health is not a static state of being. Life is a process of change, growth, and evolution. Our appearance changes as life progresses. Aging is normally associated with the corruption of the body; however, physical corruption may be a reflection of a stagnant state of our energy being. The physical body is responsive to change, especially intentional change. Free will is important.

Our physical appearance can change with the state of our being. When someone has healed, their life and their appearance may have improved dramatically, but they have not returned to a former state of health, rather they have arrived at a new state different from at any other point in their life. There may be similarities to another time, but the body is in another unique (vibrational) state of being. Getting better means embracing a new quality of life with enhanced opportunities.

I was asked to help a 91-year-old man who had been ill for some years. At the time of my first visit, he was bed-ridden, unable to stand on his own or to breathe properly. He had a shriveled and malnourished appearance, but his mind was alert. After a few energy treatments, he was up and about. One day he worked for five hours at his desk and was able to go out for a local treat. The combination of family, nursing support, energy work, and openness to shifting consciousness had a wonderful effect. Among the talks we had was a conversation regarding an understanding that the body does not have to wither in order to die.

We discussed the example of Paramahansa Yogananda, the founder of the Self-Realization Fellowship, which is based in California. On March 7, 1952, Paramahansa Yogananda entered *mahasamadhi*, which means he consciously exited his body at the time of physical death. He chose the moment of his passing, shortly after concluding a speech he had given. His passing was marked by an extraordinary phenomenon. Harry T. Rowe, the mortuary director of Forest Lawn Memorial-Park sent a letter to the Self–Realization Fellowship in which he stated: "No physical disintegration was visible in his body even 20 days after death.... This state of perfect preservation of a body is, so far as we know from mortuary annals, an unparalleled one.... Yogananda's body was apparently in a phenomenal state of immutability."

Yogananda exhibited two different levels of accomplishment. The first demonstrated what a conscious person is capable of: he ended his life with intention and without the misery of disease. His second accomplishment, of leaving his body "in a phenomenal state of immutability," demonstrated his uniquely high level of spiritual achievement.

My elder client began saying that he felt as free as a bird. Understanding our connection with our body and respecting the integration within the fabric of health generates a dignity of being.

Later, when he was intentionally in the process of letting go of his physical connection to this world, the letting go was not happening smoothly. He told his supporters that he had better begin eating again so that he could keep a healthy body as he let go. What a wonderful example of conscious awareness and flexibility!

The potential to die in health and peace demonstrates our capacity to alter our quality of both life and death. The ancient Hindus said that everything is an illusion. The idea that life runs along a predetermined course is an illusion. Consciousness can have a major influence. By using conscious awareness to understand how we are, and have been, with ourselves, we can help unravel misconceptions and illusions in our lives and make positive changes for the future.

So we see that our physical body is primarily formed and changed by our mind and emotions. Certainly the shrapnel that is held within the tissues of my body is the result of an experience with the physical world. Yet my recovery from the pain of that experience has been accomplished by means of various forms of energetic release and, most significantly, by using conscious awareness to make personal mental and emotional changes. Where surgery and medicine offered no relief, energy work and conscious awareness succeeded. We actively experience our potential when we are calm and patient, when we act openly and fairly as an expression of our own truth, and when we have the courage to hear another's truth. Learning to trust in our own resilient and flexible strength supports health on a personal level and for society as a whole.

=

7.
Breath

My experience with chronic pain reinforced my tendency to react to situations, rather than to genuinely respond to them. I'd wake up in the morning and begin reacting to life in my established vibrational patterns: medication, coffee, get busy. The days would fill up and time marched on.

I knew conscious awareness was the key, but it was a major challenge to be consciously aware and to make changes in how I felt and acted, and to develop this awareness consistently. In my studies I found that breathing was a fundamental part of almost all health systems. So I began to incorporate breathing into my process for establishing and maintaining conscious awareness in the present moment. This was a turning point - it gave me what I needed to consciously keep myself on track.

Most of us have fallen into unhealthy habits and irregular breathing is one of them. Re-training how we breathe is a simple process. And, since breathing is a natural and fundamental part of being alive, once we get the pattern re-established, it takes care of itself and requires no extra time. It is possible to experience an increased level of ease and health simply by changing how we breathe!

Conscious aware breathing is a joyous, life-enhancing practice that can work for anyone willing to commit themselves to its practice. Some benefits of aware breathing are immediate, but it also requires consistent focus. Breath is the one thing that no one can exist without. All aspects of health and consciousness can be expanded through conscious breathing.

The method by which we breathe is especially important in this high-speed society. Many people have become so caught up in moving and doing that they no longer breathe correctly. Most people breathe from their chest. Chest breathing puts unnecessary strain on the chest muscles and indirectly on the heart and lungs. Additionally, throughout the day, there are moments during which breathing can even stop. It might only last for a few seconds, until the body demands more air, but this is not a healthful scenario. This experience is normally caused by some tension in the body where the chest is held in a frozen state.

Abdominal breathing, also known as diaphragmatic breathing, generates a supportive and relaxing breath. By breathing abdominally, the floating ribs naturally lift the ribcage and there is minimal demand on the heart or lungs. Additionally, the muscular walls of the abdomen are flexing out and in, giving a very gentle massage to the organs located in this area of the body. Babies automatically do this.

Abdominal breathing is relaxing, centering, and grounding. These benefits are enhanced as abdominal breathing becomes consistent and rhythmic. The more naturally stable and grounded the body feels, the calmer it remains. Calmness is a harmonious virtue of the emotional dimension. A calm person makes better decisions (mental dimension) and the fabric of health remains steady. These dimensional threads are constantly interacting with one another and the more harmonious the energy that each has in any given moment or situation, the better is overall health. Abdominal breathing brings an important incremental increase in energy into all systems of the body: the movement of blood, digestion, elimination, clarity of mind, etc. The simplicity of nature is found in the incremental enhancement of the entire system of bioenergetic flow.

Abdominal breathing is, like all systems of nature, extremely simple and comfortable to maintain. When I practice this I sit upright with my feet on the ground. Attention is brought to the abdominal area so that one is consciously aware of all that is happening. The abdominal area begins at the pubic bone and goes up to the sternum or chest bone. Air is taken in through the nose (preferably) or mouth and into the lungs. This creates a change of pressure in the body - you can feel the abdominal area expand out as you breathe in. Notice how the ribs are lifted as the expansion spreads out. Feel the ribs float back in during exhale. This rising and falling of the abdominal muscles should be full in the sense that the breath is equally distributed. In other words, the abdomen is similar to a balloon: equal pressure and expansion is present on the back, sides, and front of the body. As I inhale, I intend and allow the gentle pressure to be felt first against my spine. To do this, feel the breathe against your spine, directly behind your navel (air doesn't just fill out into the soft muscular front of the body). Take a few breaths and notice how you can bring this gentle pressure against the spine. Practice and feel your breath. In this gentle way, we connect with how a proper breath feels.

Relax. Every action that we take is accomplished through some level of intention. Once this gentle spinal pressure is felt, allow the breath to expand out in all directions equally. Relax into feeling your breath gently stretch and align your body. Appreciate how you enhance the quality of posture and breath.

Because the upper chest area tends to hold tension, it is important to consciously fill the entire trunk of the body with breath. As the chest is expanding, I have found that it is easiest to fill the very top of the chest by imagining that the area is floating up. This helps a full breath occur. Feeling the quality of the breath integrates both mind and body into the process.

My out-breath begins as I allow my chest to fall in response to my release of air from the lungs. The falling deflates me from the top of my chest, or as high as I take the breath, back to my lower abdomen where I may choose to draw my muscles inward giving a comfortable press for full release.

A breath can be full or shallow. It is healthy for the in-breath and the out-breath to be balanced, to take in and release equally. There are many styles of breathing. This method of breathing can be ongoing throughout the day with minor attention.

The effect can be so centering that you may unconsciously shift position as the body naturally aligns itself. This will continue to occur over time; it is quite an enjoyable sensation. I still have experiences during my breathing that startle me. Everything will seem normal for a period of time, then recognition of a significant shift will occur, causing me to think: "So this is what it is all about."

The body responds to this opportunity to enhance its potential by allowing its energetic flow to align and realign. As you practice, let the experience develop, encourage it by doing some light, subtle stretching if you are comfortable doing so. Rising... falling, rising... falling, rising... falling.

Changes can be experienced as quite subtle differences in posture, or how your focus is set. The result of these moments is an advance in awareness of how the quality of life is improving. I have come to appreciate how subtle changes can have significant long-term effects.

Here is a simple awareness exercise that I incorporate into my quality time every day. Quality time is time that has conscious, purposeful awareness as its essence. I recommend a practice period of quality time at the very beginning of the day, and another at the end of the day. The length of time is not as important as the consistency of practice. Once you focus your attention, relax and take a comfortable breath. Allow and accept what is happening. Relax again and take another comfortable breath. Feel the quality of the breath. Allow the body to reposition itself if it will enhance your comfort. As you feel the enjoyment of a succession of quality breaths, you will feel and know that this is good. Continue as long as you desire.

Again, I recommend doing this at least at the beginning of your day and also at the end, when you are about to start your period of rest. Additionally, I recommend "sipping" throughout the day. Sipping gives momentary attention to the quality of breath - take one to three abdominal, or conscious, breaths and then return to your activities. Sipping does not interfere with the course of events. In fact, it enhances them.

The intention is to build toward making abdominal breathing the normal form of breath. If anything happens to startle me in the course of my day, or if I feel myself reacting to situations rather than responding to them, the very first thing I do is take a conscious breath. This requires only a second and then I am grounded, centered, and fully alive to the moment. I am ready to respond rather than to react. Try it. Your responses will be sharper, quicker, and, more consciously aware. Consciously aware breathing diffuses tension and pain while opening us more fully to the present moment.

The breath is also the basis of all the varied forms of meditation. Aware breathing can be used to develop any form of meditation, including my favorite: living life as fully as possible, now and always.

A few years ago I took myself on a meditation vacation to northwestern Thailand. I stayed at an ancient temple that is devoted to teaching Vipassana style meditation. One thing that surprised me was that almost everyone seemed to carry a small timer with him or her.

The logic of this was soon obvious. As the meditation length changed, the timer allowed one to avoid an interruptive vigilance.

In the morning, after getting ready to get into the day, check how much time is available — seven minutes, perfect. Set a timer for seven minutes and relax into a healthful seven minutes of undisturbed quality breathing. Three minutes, great! Ten or 20 minutes would be ideal, but consistency is more important than length of practice.

Equipped with a small timer that can travel with you allows quality breaks to pop into your day. When I am in New York, I often stop in Central Park for a refreshing breath break. I see how much time I have, set my timer, and soon feel quite refreshed as I continue my day. In bad weather I enjoy the quiet of a church. The more often a little time is used in this way, the greater is the quality of health.

In Thailand, seeking a place that would accept me and provide meditation support brought me to quite a variety of temples. In each one there seemed a stillness and the sensation of timelessness. Not speaking Thai, communication developed slowly. I had collected a small vocabulary, but my pronunciation was weak. It was joyful when the monks sensed how they could help me.

One day I arrived at a wonderful, remote, ancient temple where I experienced a new expansiveness of meditation and love. I still laugh when I recall my reaction to seeing everyone walking around with timers. People using timers in a land of timelessness!

=

8.
Emotion

Stress and tension in the body involves unresolved emotions. When new stresses are ignored, and the associated emotions remain unresolved, tension builds. Stress is dynamic energy that becomes caught in a contractive moment. Awareness of this dynamic energy can propel us through to a healthful expression of our self or, if it is ignored, become tension. This tension can then restrict the flow of energy in a related area of the body where it may eventually manifest itself as a health issue.

I believe that virtues are the foundation of the emotions. Virtues represent the harmonious energy of the universal spirit. As the organs transform this harmonious energy into specific virtues (attributes of calm, patience, joy, respect, love and others), these virtues form harmonious emotions. The vibrational energy of the emotions is integrated within the body through the organs. Emotions are not physically solid, yet they do have a physical presence in the vibrational patterns of our organs. We feel our emotions.

The organs are a part of the physical dimension of the fabric of health. Each organ is a field, a distinct area, of energy. Each organ has its own shape, its particular functions, and its own vibrational pattern. Just as heart rate is related to physical health, the emotional status of the heart is expressed by its vibrational tone. Disharmonious emotions begin as we stray from the virtues of our universal spirit, virtues of patience, calm, trust, respect, etc.

Prolonged tension in any one organ has a debilitating effect on energy flow throughout all the organs. Anger is an important emotion to be consciously aware of because of the physical effects it has on its associated organ, the liver. The liver is a large organ and centrally located in the body. When tension from unresolved feelings of anger builds up in the liver, energy flow is impeded. Additionally, the liver begins to heat up, affecting its performance. Heat rises, which affects the heart, the lungs, and eventually glands such as the thyroid. Each location where energy flow is disrupted contributes to additional weakness in the entire system. This all happens very subtly. The long-term effects, however, are not subtle. The gradual appearance of weakness in the energy system is commonly experienced as aging and/or illness.

We all understand a healthy heart rate, and know that emotional extremes are dangerous for someone with a weak heart. Strong emotions can be too powerful for an ill person to handle. If a friend is healthy, there is less concern about their experiencing extreme emotional highs or lows.

Chinese medicine is a well-documented and authoritative source of information for the energy flow of the organs. There are a number of conceptual models showing how emotional energy moves through successive organ energy centers. The following description of emotional energy movement is known as the "generating cycle." Of course, there are many unique variations to this cycle that reflect our individual reality. Below is a list of the dominant organs and their emotional parallels. I have listed the associated virtues and emotional equivalents together.

Heart emotions: Joy, respect, trust, love, patience, impatience, hate, non-trust or disrespect are all emotions of the heart. The energy flows from the heart to the spleen.

Spleen emotions: Fairness, openness, concern, worry, unfairness, or pensiveness (excessive mental activity), and control are all emotions of the spleen. Energy from the spleen flows to the lungs.

Lung emotions: Courage for right use of self, whole-ness, sadness, sorrow, and loneliness are all emotions of the lungs. Lung energy flows to the kidneys.

Kidney emotions: Peace, calmness, restlessness and fear are all emotions of the kidneys. Kidney energy flows to the liver.

Liver emotions: Gentle self-assertion, forgiveness, frus-tration, resentment, and anger are all emotions of the liver. Liver energy flows to the heart.

The natural flow of energy can be affected (changed to a different vibrational pattern) or interrupted due to personal attitudes, stresses, habits, confusion, or health issues.

It is appropriate to note that in different regions (i.e. Western or Eastern) the correlation between organs and emotions may vary. This is largely due to person-al and cultural beliefs regarding the meaning of an emotion. Some emotions can be the expression of two or more organs. Anxiety, for example, can result from both fear in the kidneys and non-trusting in the heart.

Organ–Emotion Chart

Organ	Harmonious	Disharmonious
Heart	patience, trust, worth, respect, love, joy, happiness	impatience, non-trust, disrespect, hate
Spleen	fairness, openness, concern	worry, pensiveness, control
Lungs	courage for right use of self, wholeness	sadness, sorrow, loneliness
Kidneys	calm, peace	fear, restlessness
Liver	forgiveness, gentle self-assertion	frustration, resentment, anger

Figure 1
The organs share a relationship with emotions (including nuances that cannot be contained within a general chart). Some emotions are an expression of two or more organs. Anxiety, for example, is a combination of fear in the kidneys and non-trusting in the heart.

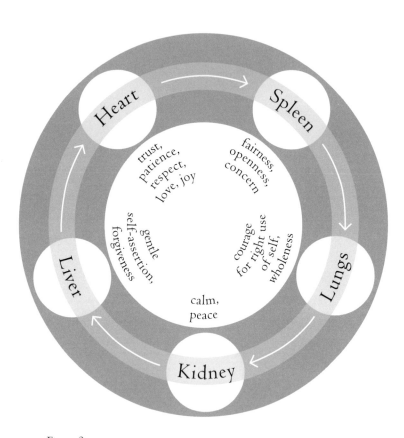

Figure 2

Emotions tend to move and cycle in patterns. When I am calm, it is easier to gently assert how I feel about something, while keeping respect for my actions in a way that is a fair and open expression of who I am. I may feel the strength of courage as I communicate my truth (how I feel) to others.

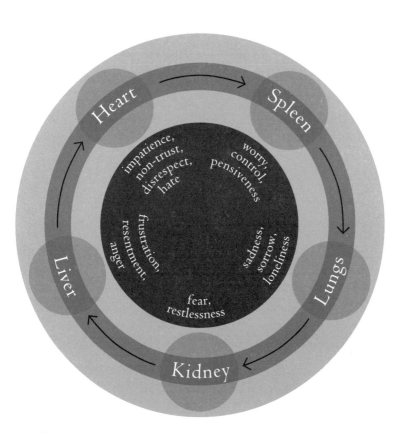

Figure 3

If I do not respect my actions, worry and loneliness can arise within me. This can cause me to feel fearful about being accepted, which brings on frustration and stress. This creates a cycle of anxiety and feeling impatient with myself, among other disharmonious emotions. I can only stabilize how I feel if I take control of my responses as much as possible and honestly express my emotions.

Emotions express the inner inclinations of a person; they are experienced personally. For instance: It is my anger. The people that I am with may sense that I am angry with them. That may be true; however, anger is first an issue within me, and of how I am feeling about myself. Emotions are a personal experience and that gives them a powerful yet subtle, long-acting, vibrational impact on the health of the body.

Of all the organs, the heart is recognized for its profound presence in emotional experiences. It is the synchronizing force among all the other organs. The heart contains knowledge of what is essential, and the emotion of love is like sweet nectar that, in its fullness, can lead the brain to wisdom. Feelings of love can attain a majestic quality.

The brain, too, plays its role in the flow of our emotions. Communications within our being flow through the central nervous system. The glands and neurons of the brain integrate the held vibrational patterns with our immediate vibrational input as we weave our expression of life in each moment.

Concious awareness affects our self-expression. Do I continue to live the limitations of my old status quo, or do I change?

People experiencing chronic physical or emotional pain usually sense at some point how non-productive and boring it can be to continue living a life of frustration, anger, and loneliness. In my case, I would catch myself falling into dark moods because of pain and the associated inability to use my body with enjoyment. The breakthrough for me was in realizing that the emotions can have a much broader range of potential expression, and through that range of expression I could release my emotional tension in a healthful and satisfying manner. Anger and frustration are not "bad" emotions, but they can create disharmony in my energy when stifled or allowed to fester without release. By gently asserting my feelings regarding that anger or frustration in an honest way, whether to others or to myself, I can release their disharmonious energy and free myself from them. This keeps my energy flow in harmony, and respects the range of emotion that can be experienced. In this way I found I could shift my mood from disharmony to harmony by living my life with a higher degree of conscious awareness.

Throughout my quest for a return to health, I was told many times to just "love myself." It sounded like a great idea, but how do I learn to love myself? The answer I have found requires rebuilding the qualities of patience and trust. I can establish patience and trust by being consciously aware and staying present in each moment. This process begins by using the breathing technique to maintain conscious awareness, and I can practice this awareness in my daily actions. When I feel anger or frustration clouding my feelings, I consciously choose to see them as signals of deeper issues. I draw in a few quality breaths and take a moment to examine where the strong feelings are coming from. If I know what is causing them I can state that truth to myself (or to another if appropriate). If I do not know the root cause, it's enough to acknowledge that the feelings of anger don't belong to the present moment, and to express patience with myself and to forgive myself for feeling them. Then I can re-engage in the present moment. I usually find the strong feelings have been lessened dramatically. This process builds patience and trust by allowing me to feel honestly about the present moment, and when I do that it releases the associated emotions and leaves me feeling open and in harmony with myself. Being consciously aware need not slow nor interrupt life's progress. Rather, it can heighten the total quality of the experience.

By continuing this practice I was able to draw on the powers of the harmonious virtues to affect how

I lived. Patience with myself became a powerful ally.
I began to be more aware of simple things, such as
the quality of my body position as I sat down, or how
I fixed a bite to eat, or read a piece of mail. Was I sitting differently if the letter was from a friend or from
the IRS?

I observed me being patient with myself as I performed
the details of life. I recognized and appreciated both
the quality this brought into each action and the effect
this patience had on me. I realized that this small change
in how I did things generated a feeling of self-trust.

Each moment of recognition enhanced my relationship with myself. These conscious moments of living
patience and self-trust form the basis of self-love. At
this stage, self-love is as delicate as a new flower.

The initial growth of things is soft and fragile. Time
and repetition enhance the feeling and other virtues
develop. Soon I felt the quality of self-respect within
me. Being more aware of myself led me to act in ways
that were more in tune with how I wanted to behave.
This process gave me an unlimited opportunity for
moments of happiness throughout the day, when I felt
the joy of making an honest choice about who I am

and how I wanted to live. Continued awareness established in me feelings of self worth. These qualities all developed because of my initial focus on patience. My fragile self-love became a strong and resilient self-love.

This process takes time, but I began to feel better and stronger in my life on a daily basis. This simple method of change has helped other people who have applied it in their lives. Yes, patience can be a large and imposing concept to address. It can also be simple — it can begin with a quality breath and an awareness of one's self in the present moment.

Now is the only moment that we are alive. Now is the only moment in which we can choose to act with patience. Neither the past nor the future are important within this moment of being patient. Simply be patient in this moment. Each now moment that we can experience in this way creates greater freedom and potential.

When the virtues of patience, trust, respect and self-worth are vibrant within, self-love can become a powerful, life-enhancing force. Observe a loving parent with their child. There is patience and a healthy trust between and within each of them. Their relationship and personal growth are in tune.

As I focused on changing the quality of my life, I knew there were deep, unresolved emotional issues within me. I could feel them, but I would hold them at bay and keep moving. The turmoil was difficult to live with; I felt miserable and that could overwhelm my ability to be present in different situations. So I started to take myself for "release walks" in the woods. I would breathe and intentionally think my way into feeling an area of emotional turmoil. I found these emotions easy to access. Just thinking of a frustration or remembering an unresolved issue would get them rolling. The emotions didn't come to me in any order, they just arose from within - anger, fear, sadness, guilt, and despair roared through me. The strong feelings, images, and pain led to a deep weeping that racked my being. I allowed the emotions to have their expression in me. After a while I would feel clear and quiet. If my mind continued to hold onto a feeling of being upset with myself or someone else, it was a signal that I wasn't done. I knew it was essential to stay focused and to develop my awareness about the release I had just gone through. I wanted to move on with my life. I was committed to real change. I appreciated myself for letting everything out and letting go of it. When I was finally feeling clear and free, I knew that I was done with that session. I continued to repeat this process until I didn't feel any more need to release. The emotional catharsis added a wonderful freedom to my life.

Just as importantly, I recognized that life is not a neat, linear process. I found it was crucial to continually recognize and acknowledge when disharmonious emotions welled up within me. Once recognized, I would again take a few conscious breaths and pause in order to sense any pertinent information that the emotions revealed. Then I was free to release the emotions and to change them into the reality that I desired.

Persistence in, and self-appreciation for, these changes not only built self-trust but also gave me greater confidence in the process itself. These experiences confirmed to me that the more fully I lived a life of harmonious emotions, the more love and eventually compassion would appear in my life. This was a stark contrast to years of suffering dark moods that had filled me with dissatisfaction and insecurity.

This is important because it is the quality of the emotions that you experience on a daily basis that can have a powerful effect on your health, personality, and the people around you. Emotions are powerful vibrations. The longer a particular emotion, say anger, is held, the more the body tends to maintain a disharmonious vibrational tone or resonance. That resonance becomes a vibrational pattern that influences everything, even the quality of cellular growth constantly happening within. A long-established emotional pattern develops into the accepted status quo, which creates automatic reactions to events. Such reactions may even feel "right" because they are so familiar; they create an established comfort zone of actions. Thus, vibrational tone can become an identification of who you are. Anger, in this example, is how you recognize yourself, and how your friends recognize you.

True happiness involves change. Yet change from the status quo is scary. Awareness, combined with trust in who we desire to be, is a basic truth to living true happiness. It is strange that moving into our true happiness should be so scary, yet the challenge of making appropriate change is where health and happiness reside.

When we flow with events and honest emotional inclinations, the body receives powerful, harmonious energy. All emotions are healthful when we act in conformity with our personal truth.

Living virtue is an authentic expression of one's self, and it constantly renews the inspiration for being alive.

Living Life with Harmonious Emotions

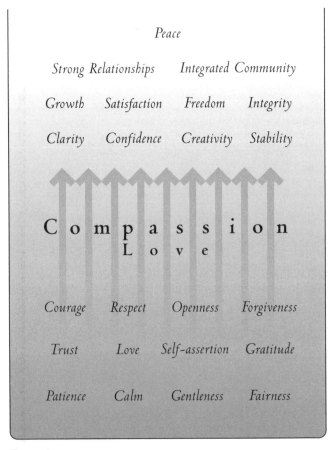

Figure 4

The harmonious emotions have an expansive energy that lifts life into the fullness of spiritual development. When fostered, they merge into the powerful emotional qualities of love and compassion, which allow and encourage the emergence of recognized qualities of a fulfilled life.

Understanding Pain With Conscious Awareness

JOHN W. CARDANO

THE FABRIC OF HEALTH

Life is *the* adventure. When physical or emotional pain becomes part of everyday reality, it can overwhelm our ability to participate in and appreciate life. But pain can also point the way to greater understanding of our selves and the further release of life's potential. Developing conscious awareness is a path to regaining true health and, as importantly, to regaining your true self.

Read the introduction of *The Fabric of Health.*

Visit www.bioenergetic-art.com

Living Life with Disharmonious Emotions

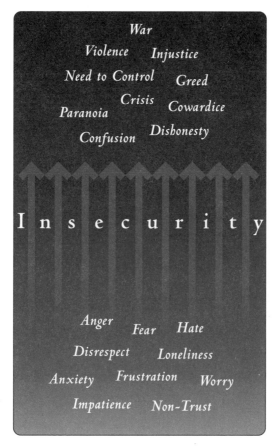

Figure 5
The disharmonious emotions have a contractive and isolating energy. These emotions merge into a feeling of insecurity that limits the potential for spirtual growth and leads to weaknesses in character.

As I live my truth in each moment, the more strongly I am consciously aware of myself. And the greater the authenticity of my expression of self, the closer I am in alignment with virtue.

When I ordered my daughter Nicole to put the wood down, I was flowing with my inner tensions – with disharmonious energy. If the emotions I act upon are not in sync with my true feelings, the inner tension from this can generate a sense of personal discomfort. And if my actions are not in sync with the expectations of others, then their reactions may bring added stress into my life.

The mind is an active participant because it stores emotional experience; the mind remembers emotional events, patterns, and attitudes. Through memory we establish accepted and respected ways of both using and responding to our emotions. When we act (or react) in an established manner, it is supported and defended by the mind. In this way, familiar (vibrational) patterns have momentum.

There are many reasons why our personal inclinations might not be accepted by those we are around. It could be a difference in maturity, experience, religion, cultural tradition, sense of responsibility, or even the disharmony that is present in the moment. Because none of these variables can be controlled by us, it becomes even more important that we act according to what we feel is right rather than to the transitory needs of a specific situation.

The mind will defend our status quo. The ego is comfortable maintaining the current state of things - it resists change. If an established pattern has given us a feeling of being secure in the past, we will utilize it in any situation where we can make it fit. Reacting with an established pattern may get us through an experience; however, we will not necessarily feel good about ourselves afterward. Our consciousness knows when we are being truthful with ourselves. So when we release emotional tension rather than react automatically to it, we move closer to personal clarity. We allow energy to flow properly in harmony with our true feelings. Emotions need not be explosive. Strong emotions like anger can be constructively released and diffused by gentle self-assertion and self-forgiveness.

For example, at the end of a busy day my partner called suggesting that we meet in town to watch a movie she wanted to see. I already had preconceived ideas about the evening, and I wanted to spend time with her. I felt anger and frustration clouding my perception. But rather than react immediately, I arranged to call her back.

I relaxed with breathing. I realized that perhaps it was my own expectations that were creating the tension, so I forgave myself for having those feelings. I also saw a way to resolve the situation into a satisfying one. I called my partner back and explained that I didn't really want to go to the movie (making that honest statement released the tension in me), but I also told her that spending the time with her was what was most important.

Communicating our feelings and consciously releasing emotional tension can open us to honest responses, without storing the stress and tension within us. Our use of the full range of an emotion in order to be expressive is empowering. Breathing and conscious awareness contribute strongly to releasing emotional tension.

When I take a breath and become clear about how I choose to be, then I am alive in the consciousness of the moment. This self-aware state of being allows me to respond to the event as the person I intend to be in my life. This does not mean that I will be "perfect." Rather, it allows me to participate as an open, dynamic human being.

As problems present themselves, we can prevent troubles by responding honestly to the moment, rather than reacting with an established pattern. In my experience, health issues and their associated pains are often related to our established patterns of reactive behavior. What a powerful force emotion is! Professional sports athletes use the power of emotion to win games. The team that maintains its emotional confidence is often victorious. All of this is a part of life. Life is the great adventure. The more consciously aware we are, the healthier and more fun the adventure can be.

=

Being Present

When do I live
The personality I desire

What need
Whose assistance
Which wind
Carries procrastination

Now
I am alive
I allow
My truth to live
Through me
Now

9.
Meditation

The path went along the side of a hill through a pine forest. The pond to my right was still, bathed in late afternoon light. Turtles were out on the north side of the pond soaking in the warm sun. Three little turtles, each one no bigger than a quarter, were on the hillside of the path, well positioned to get full benefit from the afternoon light.

I could not resist the opportunity. I followed their example, selecting a location that bathed me in sunlight while also allowing me to observe all of the turtles.

Sitting in the warm quiet of the woods, I took time to position myself comfortably, then to practice my breathing with the intention of eventually falling into a meditative state with my turtle companions.

Using quiet and an awareness of the quality of my breath allows me to observe and to control my thoughts, emotions, and urges. As I repeat this process, tensions are released from within me, and I become calmer. The periods of reflection give me an understanding of the inclinations that so often push me into old patterns of action. Breathing and meditation clear my mind and give me an opportunity to live life thoughtfully.

As dusk fell, each of us moved toward our home for the evening.

When I took my meditation trip to Thailand, I had no fixed destination for a temple in which to practice. I knew that I would find one, though - taxi drivers, innkeepers, and other locals all helped guide me with their few words of English.

In some temples the good humor and friendliness of the monks generated humor and laughter that opened everyone there to a wonderful feeling of friendship and appreciation for one another. We recognized each other as seekers of spiritual light and I enjoyed my search among the gentle Thai people and the monks of the temples.

After a week in Chaing Mai, I was recommended to a beautiful 15th century temple in the hills outside the city devoted to teaching the Buddhist practice of Vipassana meditation. I had originally planned to read and meditate on my own during this trip; however, I recognized and accepted the serendipitous opportunity being presented to me. I allowed my expectations for the meditation journey to change with the moment.

The initial learning retreat lasted 28 days. The students were mostly Thai, and I was one of the approximately 20 Westerners. Most of the Westerners were young women who had been trekking around Asia. Many with whom I spoke thought they would only stay for a 10-day trial, but instead found a peace that took them through the 28 days. Some stayed on for additional 10-day retreats. The peace and love felt at the temple allowed for an opening of one's self to occur.

One beautiful scene I witnessed was a group of four young Thai girls, about 14 or 15 years of age, who were there for a few weeks of meditation. They sat around a small stone table in the yard laughing as only young girls can. When I came by later, they were all in deep meditation. An hour later, they were all laughing wildly again.

The temple bell rang at 4am. The monks and nuns were in their respective temples chanting as the day began. During extended periods of meditation, a deep relaxation settles into you. This relaxation is deep enough that personal change can be understood and accepted.

It took me a few days to get comfortable and a few more to fully understand myself in this setting. I had come with my preconceived notions and expectations of things. Once I let go of those, my journey truly began.

Each day personal instruction was given. It was hoped that we would act on the instruction but, no matter what, we felt unconditional love. I observed other Westerners for whom it took weeks before they were ready to follow instructions. The gentle acceptance of the monks and nuns slowly opened new visitors to meditation through the joy and warmth of acceptance and love.

In Vipassana meditation there is a period of walking meditation and an equal period of sitting meditation. At first a meditation is 20 minutes, then 30, then 40, finally reaching an hour. It is hoped that the majority of the day will be passed in meditation.

During the hour of walking meditation, you are totally involved in your quality of breath and the quality of walking. There is a progressive change in the way that the foot is moved and placed on the ground. The steps are only as big as the length of your foot. You raise the foot to about ankle height and slowly move it forward, with the ball of the foot touching down first, making slight adjustments as you become comfortable.

The next hour of sitting meditation is focused on the awareness of the quality of breath combined with the placement of attention on energy points consciously integrated into the breathing meditation.

We students submitted to the intentional control of time. No reading, writing, and no, or limited, conversation. There was no enforcement of these rules, only gentle requests to stay focused on experiencing Vipassana meditation. There was a respect and love for all life and for the pace at which each person commits to their journey.

Once relaxed, I embraced the refreshment of this supportive environment. I went to 12 hours a day of meditation, and then to 16. It felt so good.

Wild experiences began to visit me. One day, not my mind, nor my emotions, nor my body wanted to participate. I was sitting in one of the temples, while my mind was pushing me to leave. I held my intention. My emotions assaulted me with impatience, anger, and an entire range of tormenting emotions – I breathed with every bit of focus on coordinating my attention on the rising and falling of my breath. Then my body would try to move out of the building – again I used the power of intention and my will to stay. I would focus on my breath. Nothing could deter my focused breathing. My state became so agitated that my body was hopping around as I meditated. After a session like that I would go outside and laugh at the insanity of my being. My mind, emotions, and body were used to having their way with me and this change took all of my focus to support.

On other days, the challenge was different. As I settled into inner stillness, my imagination presented a pleasant daydream. I noticed and focused on the rising and falling of my breath. A richer daydream appeared and again my focused breathing saved me. Well, the daydreams got richer and more enticing. The rising and falling of my breath continued to save me. The final presentation was the most fantastic sexual, full color, full sensitivity erotica that I knew I would ever experience. After a considered hesitation, I focused on my breath. Again, the gentle rising and falling of my conscious breathing removed me from my temptation.

Again afterwards I was stunned by the intensity of the push to break my journey. I remembered the temptations spoken of in *The Bible*. My temptations emerged from my memory bank of concepts on how to enjoy life. The intensive period of meditation was reframing my subconscious view of life. These periods of meditation opened me or reawakened me to a truth of the pure bliss that exists within us.

The next morning I was in a sitting meditation in the yard when I had an image of the most perfect beer. I hadn't been thinking of beer since before I arrived at the temple. Yet I had an image of a beer that totally refreshed me. I was stunned again, but in a different way. I was stunned by a sense of humor and an acceptance of what would be a pleasing reward for hard work in a hot climate. The experience matches the student's perception of enticement or reward.

I was totally enjoying the experience of Vipassana. The next afternoon, I was again deep in a sitting meditation in a temple. I suddenly could smell the most wonderful aroma of flowers. I was floating on their fragrance. Then I thought, "Someone near me must have flowers." Immediately, an incredible pain shot through my wounded knee that sent me jumping straight up and landing on my feet. I looked around. There was no one else in the temple. There were no flowers in the temple. I sat down and went immediately back into deep meditation, which again included the phenomenal fragrance of the flowers.

That evening, I told my teacher what had happened. He smiled, saying "Buddha welcomes you."

Meditation allows relaxation. This relaxation can be from the pressures of an activity, an experience, stress, or from pain in the body. Relaxation can occur at deeper and deeper levels of our consciousness and body. When tension is brought into a state of relaxation, you can reach clarity about that tension, and the tension and any associated pain can then be released.

The effectiveness of a meditation is dependent on the ability to detach from other activity. I allow myself to be free of thought. This may take a while as thoughts may continue to fill my mind. That is all right because meditation begins as a practice of breath. Thoughts come, and I lovingly renew my focus on the quality of my breath.

Meditation also becomes a method of expanding intelligence through the exploration of new horizons of consciousness. I released expectations and attitudes that had limited what I would attempt and what

I would allow in my life. I expanded into new dimensions of awareness and thought. Meditation is an opportunity to grow, to evolve, and to reach out into greater spiritual depths. A new wisdom about reality begins to replace the confusion regarding the world around us.

These new perceptions can then be quietly lived and experimented with in our own private lives as we develop an understanding of our new reality. Consciousness is not a static state. Consciousness grows and evolves as we stretch ourselves to expand our understanding of life.

=

Calm

the morning bell pulls me into a day of meditation
monks and nuns chant in their respective temples
4am begins each day's journey of self-exploration
slowly deliberately I walk for an hour into awareness
then sitting I allow another hour of meditation
walking sitting walking sitting for an hour each
a pause for personal hygiene
10:30am we share the day's meal
perhaps a half hour of conversation with other explorers
the wooden floor of a temple carries me through my next hour
the temple floor becomes my cushion for sitting meditation
hours buoy me in peaceful silence
walking sitting floating on breath to blissful peace
such practice alters my perceptions of this world
a calm previously unknown opens my sight
abilities are within each person to create
a reflection of their state of presence
what a blessing to create from calm
clarity joy love compassion
gifts of calm presence
calm peace calm
fruits of life
free to all
peace
calm
calm
peace
solid base
foundation
for quality life
growing to fullness

10.
A Pivot

Upon leaving the temple of my Vipassana retreat, my meditation experience had opened my eyes to a new view of the city, fabulously rich in temples and spiritual support. Before, I had appreciated its beauty, but now I was drawn to it.

So much had happened to change and enhance my awareness of life. I realized that during this month of spiritual quest that my pain had not maintained its consistent or deep pattern. My focus on expansive harmonious states of being had released tensions in my body that had been holding onto my pain. Of course it is not possible to live everyday in a temple, yet the experience confirmed the profound effects of integrating conscious awareness into my life. The enhancement of my vibrational harmony and the opening of my energy to personal growth are rewards enabled by the process of realigning the threads of my existence.

The spiritual dimension is the presence that exists throughout every living thing. It is universal; a divine spark in us all. We can make that spark grow stronger and brighter through conscious awareness. Since spiritual energy is beyond time, there is no schedule to our personal growth agenda. There is only self-discovery, renewed clarity, and eventual personal evolution.

Thus the thread of spirit provides a pivot point for the experience of life, a steady guide throughout time. The physical, emotional, and mental threads each go through continuous change, and the presence of the spirit provides a quiet, consistent, and dependable beacon.

My train was leaving at 6pm. I decided to do a day of meditation through the city. I found myself at a temple that had drawn me before I began my meditation course. There was a large, impersonal, if not unpleasant, monk who sat at the front of the temple and watched. It felt unusual, as the other temples did not have such an obvious guard.

I entered and seated myself. I was drawn to ask Buddha for assistance in growing my consciousness. It was a wonderful meditation. An expansive quality of connectedness resonated within me. Upon finishing, I rose to leave. Much to my surprise, the large monk silently greeted me bowing in a pose of warm and appreciative brotherhood.

I found myself walking through temple grounds and parts of the city that were unfamiliar. I felt as though I was there, everywhere, and nowhere all at once.

As I walked through the grounds of yet another temple, I stopped beside a stone staircase that led up the side of a huge pedestal upon which rested a smaller temple. I walked up the turning staircase that gave entrance to a foyer. There were three smaller rooms off a central area. Immediately to my left was an area devoted to the royal family. Directly in front of me was an elaborate altar with a golden Buddha. To my right was another elaborate altar with an ivory Buddha. Each room was exquisitely created, fine workmanship visible in every ornate detail.

The central area, which joined the four rooms, was in the shape of a lotus flower, the perfect symbol of our ability to evolve from darkness into light. Intricate woodcarving depicted the relationship between nature and the divine. The light bounced through the temple as though it were alive, like magic in the air.

Visitors often bring gold leaf with them to the temples. They place it onto the images of Buddha. Some images of Buddha eventually become completely covered in layers of gold leaf.

Occasionally, the gold leaf is attached only along one edge so that it becomes a golden flag gently moving in a breeze. The reflection of sunlight dances with the movement of the golden flags. In time, the golden flags begin to break up into little golden flecks that swirl in the air adding floating reflections of sunlight. The beauty of this was expansive. When I noticed being speckled with golden flecks, I laughed with enjoyment at the generosity of life.

The day was quite hot and I was alone in the temple. I felt invited to step to the center of a plush lotus rug that covered the central area. I seated myself between two images of Buddha and slipped into meditation.

I soon felt the presence of another. Opening my eyes I observed a man seating himself directly in alignment with me. He sat at the edge of the rug about six feet away. We gazed into each other's eyes until there was serenity between us. I returned to my meditation.

After a few moments he began to sing. His voice was extraordinary. His song lasted for a full meditation with changes in timbre, pace, range, vibrato — it was extraordinary.

The words did not repeat. I opened my eyes to see him holding a multi-faceted clear crystal orb. It was then that I understood that he was intentionally sharing an alchemical ceremony with me.

I dropped back into my meditation, which was being enhanced by his vocal alchemy. He was creating a talisman. The crystal sphere would be transformed into a potent, energized object through his intention, meditative prowess, and the vibratory power of his song.

Once more, his voice shifted so that I was drawn to open my eyes. He was in the process of moving the orb from one position of energetic alignment to another in a full series of power points around the body.

I finished my meditation a little before he finished his. When I was ready, I opened my eyes. The orb was no longer a clear crystal. It now was a beautiful, almost opaque golden crystal. Luminous golden yellow is the color of intelligence and wisdom.

I rose and moved to sit on a chair in the alcove. A young boy monk greeted me with a smile from his chair opposite me.

The other man walked out to sit on the stairs and put on his boots. I had not noticed his green fatigues earlier. I went out and stopped as I passed him. We shared the same silent communication as before to a mutual serenity. We bowed and I departed. I was surprised and delighted to learn from his uniform that he was a very high-ranking military officer.

I thanked Buddha for the speed with which he answered my prayer for assistance in growing my consciousness.

For many of us the spiritual thread transcends time. One of the essential means of expressing the spiritual in this world is through the virtues. Moral codes may differ, but virtues and values of life are common throughout all societies. These universal virtues and values include trust, patience, respect, honor and freedom.

During my youth I had thought that virtues were a demanding ascetic law that a wrathful god demanded of us, and that they limited who I could be and what I could do. How wrong I was.

Virtues do not limit individual expression - they free it. Trust in oneself, for instance, can be a powerful force in our lives if we consistently feel that we act in accordance with our personal integrity. Once we recognize that we can trust ourselves, it builds confidence. Confidence can then become a powerful force in our lives. When we feel these qualities strongly within us, our capacity for experiencing joy and happiness is greatly expanded. Ah, such an adventure!

The clear crystal that transformed into a golden orb is an example of the power that focused spiritual qualities can bring into our lives. Each of us can use the guidance of the spirit within us to gently and slowly improve our quality of life as we consciously move toward a fuller, happier, and healthier existence.

=

II.
The Weaver

By committing to observe myself and to live with more clarity regarding whom I intended, and still do intend, to be, deep insights about my life came forth. Through this process I came to know The Weaver. The Weaver is the consciousness within us, and it is capable of observing the tiniest aspects of the self while seeing the fullness of our being. The Weaver forms us by bringing together our most powerful assets: intention, attention, will, desire, belief, imagination, reason, intuition, attitude, memory and our innate potential. These tools organize how we grow as a result of the vibrational quality in our thoughts, moods, and actions.

When I was first ready to make changes in my life, my mind railed at the difference between who I had become and who I believed myself to be. I wondered what had happened to the person who I thought had so much potential?

Not everyone saw me the way I saw myself. Some saw an old friend with whom they had shared good times. Others saw a dependable worker who was trusted to perform necessary tasks. Still others saw a man who was getting through life despite the effects of having been to war.

These and other images of me contained an element of truth. Yet when I looked at myself in the mirror, I felt the totality of who I was and, more importantly, of who I was not. Just as in the story *A Christmas Carol*, Scrooge experiences different views of himself through the visitations of the spirits. My reflection in the mirror inspired a conscious awareness of myself that was the essence of Scrooge's enlightenment. It was a life changing reality check. There I was in the mirror without my soul.

I knew how I had arrived at my situation. It had not been a singular evil deed. It had been the result of years of living an illusion. I treated my personal relationships the same way I did the pain in my body — by ignoring them. In my attempts at communication I left out the most essential communication - I left out any clarity about how I felt and what I needed.

My intention to communicate with more clarity established a new tone in my life as I became a more active participant in creating new ways of being. This tone affected my will to act, as well as the intention that motivated my actions. This ultimately led to a review of my attitudes and beliefs. My believing that my status quo was acceptable was as wrong in my life as it had been for Dickens' Scrooge.

Aware breathing became a major ally in changing and improving my health. This put me in tune with The Weaver, and I began to see how I was growing. Getting to know myself on a fundamental level was like making a new best friend. I began to have increased awareness of the harmony or disharmony in how I felt (my vibrational resonance), which I experienced as comfort or discomfort with myself and with my actions.

My awareness allowed me to realize when I was being an effective observer of the details of my life. My marriage, for example, involved me on every level; it affected the emotional, mental, and physical fibers of my being on a daily basis, as well as my spiritual sense of what I felt was right. Like a strand in the fabric, it surfaced again and again. In one place it could be supportive, in another dynamic, and in another, where there were weaknesses, troublesome.

The quality of our consciousness is expressed through our personality. The choices we make in determining our behavior become integrated into our subconscious patterns. Our personality mirrors the truth about how we see ourselves, and social interaction can give us insight into the state of our maturation. We can sense how others respond to us. All the things we do without conscious effort are in our subconscious program.

Like many other people, I was able to live my life with pain and disabilities without drawing attention to them. What I lost was the quality of being truthful. I was being inauthentic, initially with my self, and then, automatically, with others. This was not about being deceitful for any personal gain, but deceit became part of my subconscious behavior. I learned that how I treat myself becomes the model for how I treat other people.

The subconscious is the most dedicated servant anyone could desire. The subconscious does not hesitate to act in the way it has been trained. When my actions are not a truthful expression of the person I feel myself to be, my subconscious rationalizes the correctness of my behavior. Allowing this process to continue means living a non-aware life.

The Weaver, which is active in us through our intuition, is, like a gentle breeze, easily ignored. I had known that things were not right in my life, but a strong will and rationalization can overwhelm the subtle recognition of intuition. Denial provides further support for the rationalization of behaviors. By ignoring intuition, my sense of inner peace and harmony was lost: I kept taking medication and pushing along. By not honoring my intuition, the flow of vibrational energy became impeded and subsequently affected the related organs. I sensed a growing weakness in me, though I still found some reprieve in finishing a project, taking more medication, or sleeping.

The Weaver, my consciousness, perceived all this when I looked into the mirror. That was a moment of self-conscious awareness, which was the result of a powerful sense of agony. Personal change is, unfortunately, often motivated by the experience of physical or emotional agony. Once we are moving along the track of life, it can take a momentous event to derail us and make us recalibrate who we are. In this way we can recognize traumatic events in our lives as complex experiences. Life exposes us to unexpected changes, some are painful, others are sweet. When these events are experienced with awareness, it allows for personal growth that can be both recognized and appreciated. By accepting the fullness of our being, difficult losses can be softened.

Years of silencing my intuition and feeling dishonest with myself created knots in my energy fields. These knots impeded growth within my physical body, which eventually affected my cells, tissues, and physical and mental abilities – all of me. Under such conditions, when a health problem might emerge is a mystery. Still, most people do sense a subtle discomfort or uneasiness within themselves, and somewhere in their self-conscious lurks the silent wish to change.

Many of our decisions in life are driven by our perception of security, or lack of it. Acting according to an established pattern is often based on the hope that security will result. Such security may be real, temporary, or false hope.

Trusting in and following my intuition doesn't mean that every answer will always be clear the moment I desire it. Often there is a pause, or interval of time, without feedback, and a particular issue may remain unresolved for an extended period. During this time, I have noticed that other dimensions of my personality are evaluating and building trust in my complete willingness to await an option that feels right to me and then commit to it. All of me is involved in changing. Building trust is different than simply going ahead with whatever options are available.

A willingness to change enabled me to transform my subconscious patterns. The subconscious accepts a change in the same way that the pattern was originally set: a purposeful decision is made to change how I act, and I maintain awareness of that change in my thoughts and actions again and again. Conscious repetition, by my consciously aware self, allows me to reset my subconscious patterns and to behave more as I intend to be.

At various times in my life I have tried different ways of doing things, only to abandon them and return to familiar ways. It is human to seek alternate methods of doing something. Still, it requires clear, intentional persistence to change established subconscious patterns.

My intention to change awakened my conscious awareness, but it did not keep it constantly on guard. Time moves along and suddenly I might realize that I am doing exactly what I said I would no longer do. Such is life. Old habits are tough patterns to break. Part of the process is to continually appreciate myself for noticing the habit in progress. That awareness reinforces my commitment to change. Judging myself does not enhance change; rather judgment can return me to an old pattern of acting with personal disrespect.

I have learned to become aware of myself at the earliest stages of reverting to an old pattern. These are empowering moments, and in them my self-conscious is able to reframe how I live an experience. Over time I have felt the benefits of a new emotional stability growing within me.

Conscious change for personal health requires sacrifice. Self-sacrifice is usually understood as sacrificing oneself for the good of others. In truth, self-sacrifice is about changing how one lives in order to become the person you believe yourself to be. By sacrificing the comfort of the status quo within yourself, and living an intentional change, you can become that person.

These changes are difficult, yet every day they strengthen my personal sense of trust. A strong level of trust is key to creating self-love. And self-love generates emotional strength and imparts a wonderful lightness to our lives.

In this way, I do not sacrifice my strength for the well being of others. Instead, the powerful resonance of who I am intentionally becoming is shared with the universal spirit of all others. Such evolution requires an awareness of myself being The Weaver in my life, and maintaining a humble appreciation for creating the person I desire to be.

When a dear friend suffered the loss of a loved one, I felt myself torn by trying to support her emotional turmoil, while at the same time honoring the integrity of my emotions. Though I have known and felt the sadness and loneliness that comes from losing a loved one, those feelings had attained a different resonance within me. I did not want to experience, nor did I believe in, the same vibration of mourning that I sensed within her. It may have been much easier to simply join her in her mourning, but then I would not have been living my personal truth in that situation.

I sensed that my friend felt I was not being supportive of her sadness and loss. I respected her right to grieve in her way, though that did not lessen my friend's expectation of me to emotionally journey with her. I was living in one of those pauses in time between following my intuition and succumbing to another's needs. Still, I resolved to stay emotionally true to myself and trusted my intuition. Days later we had the opportunity to discuss what had happened, and we shared our feelings. Once we came to understand and accept each other's viewpoints, everything moved beyond the pause and our friendship benefited from the experience.

In such situations it is easy to feel that resolution depends upon the other person. That is not the case. The only way I can establish harmonious vibrational resonance and support my coming into a fuller realization of myself is by reaching personal clarity. That quality of clarity generates an inner peace that supports me in my growth and then vibrates out to others — especially to those involved in the event.

Each subtle improvement affects my recovery. My wounding had a powerful impact on my entire being. Each time I claim or reclaim another aspect of who I intend to be, my health improves. I am amazed at the wonderful qualities that a simple change can bring into life. My healing requires much more than what is visible. Healing integrates all of the fabric of health. All the dimensions of my pain communicate information to The Weaver.

The Weaver is consciousness and consciousness is an active connection with everyone and everything. The Weaver is like the sun: even though it is far away, we cannot exist without its effects in our life. Everything is connected, all I can do is to become clearer about who I can be and, as I live it, improvement happens.

=

My Path

birds return from some distant journey
brilliant colors and soothing calls fill the trees
nests are being repaired
such exuberance throughout their world
how do they soar along the path with such ease

my path has twists and unexpected turns
time disappears during those moments
blood runs through me with such speed
my heart brain – all of me
may remember a flash of a scene
yet incomprehension fills me to the brim
who is the person traveling this path
to where am I being led

whistling as I perch on a park bench
I return a call from the trees
the scent of fresh blossoms
lifts me higher into a temporary nest
participating in song with unseen birds up high
my spirit feels at home within the Oneness
relaxed presence flowing with nature reveals
unanticipated pleasures on my path

12.
The Time is Now

We all experience time in many forms. Greenwich Mean Time runs the business and social world, nature has its seasons and, of course, there is our own personal experience of time.

Our relationship with time is important – it can affect the fabric of health. The passage of time can feel like a stress that cannot be escaped. In this high-speed computer age the most common reaction to time is - "Why isn't it done yet?" and "I can't wait." When in a rush, it always seems like time is running out.

The experience of time also can be affected by anticipation. This is a form of non-linear time. Driving to a new location always seems longer than the return trip. When waiting, time often drags.

On a cold winter day I was hiking with my dog, Tomo. Stopping for a rest, Tomo, a wonderful Rhodesian ridgeback, walked onto an ice-covered precipice. In an instant he slid out into mid-air. Tomo appeared to stand on air as he looked around at the absence of ground under his feet. He looked back at me like a cartoon character saying "oops," and then dropped out of sight. Luckily, there was deep, soft snow at the bottom of a 20-foot drop. Tomo was fine, so it was easy to have a good laugh. During an intense experience time seems to stop, and my perception of that moment had stretched into minutes.

Personal time is my reference to my experiences and what may have happened on a given day. The day my daughter Nicole was born is an unforgettable date, as was my graduation day, or the day I was wounded. For everyone there are many events: a wedding, a funeral, or a national disaster like 9/11. Our life events become markers in personal time.

Time is essentially experienced as a mental system for tracking what is happening in life. Yet it is the quality of life during time that is important. Now is the only moment that I am alive. Being present to the moment opens me to personally important perspectives. I am more effective in the moment when I am aware of intention, responsibility, and the state of my potential. Acting in this moment, now, is me at my most effective.

There is also the more expansive experience of spirit time. For a Native American, intentional connection with the spiritual world is a wondrous event. Spirit time is a time capsule within "normal" time. It is

similar to a dream or a vision during which an entire
journey can occur, and upon returning to normal time
only a few moments may have passed. Such spiritual
time can have a profound effect on the perspective of
the journeyer.

There are also the larger celestial periods all the way
up to ages, which are almost 2200 years in length.
The dawning of the Age of Aquarius has been oc-
curring for at least 30 years. The ages are defined by
the alignment of celestial bodies that have a vibrational and gravitational effect on all of us. It is like
the effect that our moon has on the tidal movement
of the oceans.

The Piscean Age, which is in its dusk, is represented
by two fish swimming in opposite directions and is experienced as the effects of dualism: right and wrong,
war and peace, one belief system versus another belief
system. The appropriate tool for the Piscean Age is
judgment.

The Aquarian Age is represented by a figure pouring
water, everything flowing together. The movement into
this age has been signaled by changes around the world.
The computer age is enhancing communication. The

speed of ideas and travel has made the world a smaller place. Changes are taking place on a global scale.

Still, now is the only moment in which something can actually be done. If we expand our understanding about what is happening now, it allows us to release the tensions of anticipation or worry.

Of course, reflecting on the past helps us to understand life's patterns, to know what to build on, and to know what would be best to change. Taking time to plan for the future has great benefit. These are all valid, conscious activities of now time. However, as a need occurs, those thought processes must end so we may be fully engaged in the event of the moment.

If we spend time in judgment or disapproval of ourselves regarding events from the past or fears about the future, we are in a time trap. Time traps are wasted moments of precious "now." Not only is life opportunity wasted when we dwell in a contractive mental and emotional posture, the harmonious energy flow of the body is effectively being short-circuited.

When it comes to health, our personal experience of time also includes transition time. This is the period that is required to recover from unforeseen problems such as traumatic events or injuries. Trauma can be physical, emotional, mental or any combination of these. There are three types of transition time: recuperative, regenerative, and transformational.

Recuperative time passes when we are assessing and healing after a trauma. We often allow ourselves the barest minimum of time to stabilize our health and then we get right back into our old ways of doing things. In some cases, we even step up our efforts in order to make up for our injury down time. Obviously, such actions imply that the activities themselves are more important than the quality of our health.

Regenerative time is the period after recuperation where we incorporate our new health status into our lives, whether it means regaining a physical ability, an emotional stability, or a mental capacity. Many of us have observed people whose injury caused them to walk off balance, perhaps leaning to one side. A condition such as this can persist even though no structural problem can be found. Twenty years ago I would pick up my right shoe and shake my head at what I saw: the outside edge and side leather would be worn away, while the bottom of the shoe was almost new. The left foot had similar wear, though not as bad.

There wasn't a structural problem with me, I was compensating for the pain in my leg while pushing to move along. The shoes got me thinking. I began focusing on the way I walked and on my physical alignment. I started putting my hands on the tensed muscles to help them relax. Stretching and being aware of how I placed my foot also became important. Focusing on my breath helped to calm me and to keep my attention on realigning my body. Even now I observe how I place my foot when I walk. It is important to maintain this awareness as my injuries can still act up, causing muscle spasm, pain, and a twisting of my leg.

Attention to these details is worthwhile: my life improves. My steady intention of walking correctly has benefited my posture, the overall quality of my movement, and is an aware integration of my current state that bolsters my confidence.

It is now over 36 years since my injury. Some of my health problems were temporary. Others are chronic, long-term issues. Regardless, quality-of-life improvements are a valuable ongoing effort. These efforts have become part of my lifestyle. My condition has improved and I can go for longer periods of time with a wonderful ease of being. My focus stays on expanding the quality, fullness, and enjoyment of life.

Regenerative time will not take me back to being a healthy 20-year-old. Rather it moves me forward: The focus of my journey is in improving my understanding of myself as I increase the enjoyment of using my body. Understanding and appreciating the person I am becoming reinforces valuable self-confidence.

During this process we can still accomplish what we feel are necessary responsibilities, yet it is also important to balance them with attention to our health. This includes an effort to incorporate the lessons and observations about our selves that come to our attention. This may require a period of special diet, rest, and an appreciation of the changes in our actions.

In the final stages of regenerative time, we are at least as constitutionally healthy as we were before the injury. Additionally, our performance and quality of life has improved. The improvement is a result of personal, intentional changes that we have made in life due to lessons from the event itself. There may be physical abilities that are not recovered, but that is more than offset by the fullness of who we have become.

Regenerative time overlaps and stabilizes into transformational time. Transformational time begins when we consciously participate in the changes in our lives. We become fully committed and engaged in living a consciously aware life in the present moment. Transformational time ends, perhaps, with death.

For me, trying new ways in which to work toward health helps me gauge my mental and emotional progress. I spent a few years getting into bicycle riding. I used a recumbent bicycle (designed so that the rider is sitting low with the legs pushing forward at hip level) to ease the strain on my body. It was a fun and challenging effort. Sometimes my efforts generated gains in conditioning, other times a little too much effort aggravated my old injuries and meant weeks of realigning myself.

One summer I organized an exercise program of walking or running in the ocean. Being in the water took stress off the body and I was able to improve my cardiovascular strength and physical tone.

When I first arrived at the beach, a friend invited me out on his motorboat. I leaned over the bow to release the mooring line, a reach of two to three feet, depending on the waves, only to find myself fighting to stay on board the boat. My balance and abdominal strength weren't all that I expected them to be. I struggled to perform this fairly simple task. I did manage to release the line and get back aboard — barely.

After practicing my runs in waist-deep water, I was able to perform the mooring duties with agility. By using different techniques and finding the appropriate balance of effort and flow, I am able to become more aware of myself in any moment. All improvements are a lift in happiness. These experiences teach me a great deal about myself. Taking time to understand my current abilities, to incorporate improvements, and to intentionally expand my awareness opens me to a passion for life.

As I continue to follow my intuition and live in the present moment, my experience of time has changed, expanded, and, sometimes, disappeared. Miracles happen. Transformational time for healing blends into all the time of life.

=

13.
Humor

Creating contentment and joy in our lives is necessary refreshment. Laughter and crying both provide a healthful release from emotional and physical tension. A good belly laugh or a good weeping cry shakes the body out of its prevailing state.

I have found great pleasure in both a good body shaking laugh or cry. My preference, of course, is laughter, because when the shaking is done, I am in a happy, open frame of mind. Weeping is wonderfully cathartic, but it does require considerable discipline to go through the restorative process of appreciating the issue at hand and shifting to a more comfortable emotional place. It requires changing from one state on the emotional continuum to another, perhaps moving from the emotional states of sadness, fear, and worry, to being calm, open, and appreciating what a specific issue has meant in my life.

There have been times when frustration has clouded my day because of something that didn't happen, or something I forgot to do. When I find myself upset about something going on in my life, I seize upon that recognition as a cause for humor - a chance to laugh at how human I can be. Being upset and staying that way only deepens my problem. I am now able to appreciate the silliness of so many of my stresses. Being upset is not going to help. But I do know that releasing tension gives almost every situation a greater opportunity to improve.

Since life is a great adventure, we should treat it that way. When heroes like Zorro, Indiana Jones, or even a fish like Nemo are up against the wall, they draw on the virtues of self-confidence, humor, gentleness, courage, and trust. Abnormal tension has no home here. The hero freely flows with the situation. His sensitivity to the moment allows him to find a way through the chaos and live to see another day.

The villain, however, is doing everything possible to control the situation. With enough overwhelming power, such control can work, but it is never a stable situation. Control fosters worry, which is an unbalanced state. The situation eventually falls into chaos and the process of chaos grants energy to the individual that is balanced and flexible.

Humor can be described as the ability to perceive, enjoy, and/or express what is amusing or incongruous. Another definition is the ability to feel such ease of being that one laughs readily. This is not laughing at anything; rather it is feeling so good that laughter is an automatic release of pleasure.

Great humor for me is based on innocence and ease of being. Spending time with children often brings laughter and joy. The innocent flow of energy and action is refreshing and freeing. Kittens and puppies display a similar presence as the purity of their uninhibited jumping and rolling about releases cries of pleasure and fits of laughter from anyone watching.

Tomo, our much-loved dog, enjoyed playing his own version of catch - it was "catch me if you can." We would play one on one or with a large group. With a group, we would form a circle with Tomo in the middle. He was 28-inches at the shoulders and 115 pounds of solid muscle. Try as we would, no one could catch Tomo.

Tomo could dart at high speed through one person's legs with his body conforming to some non-existent tunnel on the ground, spin around, fake another way while changing directions in response to a few new chasers and always come right back into the circle. Eventually, everyone would finish exhausted and laughing.

The pleasure of being at ease with one's inner being generates spontaneous laughter. It can happen while walking alone, and in apparently incongruous situations. It is an independent, expansive feeling of joy. As with the appreciation of inner growth, you are your own audience. For me, laughter is common when I meditate on a consistent and regular basis.

Humor and ease of being are not dependent on meditation, however. Living an aware lifestyle where one is flexible and consciously chooses ease over tension also cultivates humor. Being able to laugh at the things I do, and the circumstances that I may find myself in, releases tension and opens me to flow with life.

Being stiff, ill at ease, and fearful of what will happen next exaggerates the potential for problems. Fear is the unbalanced emotion of the kidneys. The harmonious state is peace and calm. A personal sense of peace and calm provides a foundation for harmony throughout the entire fabric of being. Such a harmonious state supports a smooth flow of energy and thus enhances the potential for a harmonious outcome.

Humor and laughter have been recognized for their healthful effects and provide a powerful tool to be consciously structured into life.

=

14.
Our Adventure

.

This grand adventure called life starts with creation. Creation stories from different cultures speak of the almighty forces of the heavens creating and merging with the powerful force of the Earth.

A series of fabulous events occur in the wondrous process of creation. According to Native Americans, after the first few events of creation, several water animals worked together to gather soil from the deep bottom below the water that covered the planet. These were courageous actions performed for the good of continuing creation.

After great effort, a small amount of soil was placed on the back of a turtle. This soil then grew in volume until it became Turtle Island, or North America. Later some of this soil was formed into humans. Spirit was breathed into them and according to the type of nature essence associated with the spirit, each of the tribes was created. Thus powerful and mysterious forces combine. The magic of the union creates us. We are dust and spirit.

Every culture presents their vision of creation, where the creator creates everything. Modern science proves that everything is connected. The Age of Aquarius that we are entering will bring an experience of oneness. My healing experience has caused me to recognize and respect the integrated fabric of my being and to feel the oneness of everything.

The wonder of divine power is always with us. Each of us is a spark of the divine. The degree of inner clarity with which I live my life affects the quality of my integration with the divine spark. My health adventure has taught me that my body is the final message center for understanding how to live my life.

Intuition is the first communication link to the magic of life. It is such a delicate form of knowing that I can be confused about its truth. When I am attempting to be sensitive about how to act, I can wonder if I am confusing intuition with my old patterns of doing things. My habits may feel right, but intuition is true spiritual guidance. Because of this, I can discern the difference between intuition and old patterns by recognizing which guide is more virtuous. Ultimately, only one guide will always leave me feeling good about myself.

Such a degree of conscious awareness is a developed ability in itself. Even habits can be overwhelmed by inner proclivities and unexpected events. The adventure, after all, has mysterious developments.

Health problems are symptoms that help us to understand the issues that trouble us. Symptoms send a message that something needs to be changed. Sensitivity, observation, patience and willingness to change are key to our transformation and healing.

When there is discomfort in my body, I make adjustments. Developing my awareness and respect for health supports me in making quality changes. My growth has been incorporated into my experiences of the pressures and pleasures of the world.

Chronic health problems normally develop over a period of time. Good medical care is essential and modern medicine provides important services. The fact that there are wonderful and qualified health professionals who provide essential services, however, does not release us from the responsibility of participating in our life and in our own health.

Understanding a health issue is not simple. The average person is quite resilient. Tensions and troubles in the body are things that we acclimate to and accept. They are like a little white lie that doesn't go away. After many years it festers until it creates enough havoc that it must be dealt with. Too often, the issue underlying a symptom of ill health may be long buried and forgotten, and unlikely to even be given any consideration. The surface issue that arises as the presenting problem is what we normally respond to and treat.

In many cases, this is acceptable. The presenting issue can be dealt with and a complete resolution can happen in its own time. Still, the symptoms of ill health need to be respected as important messages and not suppressed or eliminated as an end in itself. The relationship between problem and consciousness is rarely clear. Each part of the body is a vibrational component that can be traced back to an associated organ that is related to an aspect of consciousness. The individual is the only source for true comprehension of their issue. Such insights require a developed level of awareness.

Symptoms can be changed or even cured in the process of healing the issue that they represent. If we provide support for the body to reassert its innate intelligence in as many ways as possible, we are living an aware participation in life and tending to the fabric of our health.

Health issues affect all dimensions of our being that are subject to change: physical, emotional, and mental. The spiritual dimension is infinite and unchanging; its presence within us can be strengthened and developed.

A comprehensive approach to health can yield amazing results. The process may include physical adjustments, nutritional support, as well as mood and attitudinal changes. Our efforts can take us to a new level of life. Consciously appreciating the process of change is extremely beneficial: I encourage, accept, and acknowledge my efforts.

Personal awareness of one's inner qualities is the essence of true humility, based on a personal honesty with who we know ourselves to be. Self-knowledge of who we are grows and changes as we live our truth. Such qualities are felt within and automatically radiate out into our life.

Recognition of our efforts builds self-esteem and confidence. Confidence is a quality of character that gives fundamental power to our personality. But true confidence is experienced as quiet self-recognition - it is not dependent on any outside perceptions. Confidence comes from living our truth and experiencing the personal benefits that gradually come from such quality of living.

My personal awareness of being who I choose to be during any moment of life yields contentment. Life can often seem a series of mundane moments. Yet these moments link together to create something special. It could be a day of work, a trip to the store, or any normal event. Each is a collection of moments, the vast majority of which can be mundane. But it is the qualities of these moments that generate the quality of the event and the quality of life.

Living one's inner qualities, qualities that had been abandoned or never before allowed expression, can change even the most mundane moments into extraordinary experiences.

Emotions charge our actions with passion and power. Power is expressed in many ways: hurricane winds or the growth of a fingernail both exhibit power. The scale of power does not limit its effectiveness.

In the past when I felt fear, it would alter my potential to live fully. Now when I feel fear, I become excited because I know that I am in a position to develop my ability to live fully. I breathe, calm myself, and observe if there really is anything to fear. Calm is the harmonious state of the emotion fear. More often than not, my fear is an illusion based on some unfounded insecurity. Once I am clear about the situation, I can move beyond my fear and enter a new and expanded quality of life.

It is important to be aware of emotional reactions during any event. Is my emotional state consistent with how I intend or desire to live my life? Is this intention an awareness of truth?

Understanding the ability to shift emotions can contribute greatly to reducing confusion regarding any issue or situation. Confusion dilutes our essential power. The process of reducing confusion yields health and growth. My reality is a reflection of my emotional state and my mental conditioning.

The truth expressed by the ego is often an accommodation for living the status quo. Real truth is an alignment with virtue that is harmonious with universal principal. Universal principal has a consistency that can be observed throughout all of time.

Real truth is like the breath and conscious attention: it has a subtle presence that sustains and invigorates all of life. It creates a harmonious environment that vibrates with the resonance of truth and supports health. All of us are constantly creating new cells. In a harmonious environment the new cells are of an increasingly healthy nature. The vibrational resonance of cellular quality is displayed in the beauty of youth or through improved health. As each individual consciously grows in these gentle ways, they participate in the creation of health for themselves and for society as a whole.

Thus the quality of the emotional state is reflected in the quality of the physical state. There is no room for judgment, only awareness, making appropriate changes, and living a fulfilling life. Life is a process of evolution for each and every one of us. Instead of judgment, simple acts that demonstrate and teach the effect of living a conscious life can bring about great change and progress.

The fabric of health is an enormous art form to master. Patience, respect, and inner peace gradually build a framework that produces the personal confidence necessary to be a master artist. Life is an experiential journey along a full and often turbulent path of growth.

In working with people troubled by "incurable" health issues, there has rarely been a sudden dramatic healing. There is continuous movement toward health and appreciation of self. Cancer, Alzheimer's Disease, and depression have all responded to conscious vibrational change. This change manifests itself as an increase in vibrational harmony, which in turn creates an ease of being. The state of ease affects the thoughts, intentions, philosophies and all other aspects that compose the consciousness. Being at ease with oneself is a basic element of health that affects one's auric field of energy.

My auric field is a like a snapshot of my health. My total being generates an aura of vibrational energy that hovers in the ether around me. This vibrational aura affects my etheric blueprint. Just as a blueprint determines the final form of a building, my auric field sets and resets the pattern of my physical body as I change and evolve.

The elements I describe are non-material realities of my present self, and they truthfully represent the degree to which I have been rigid or flexible, closed or open regarding my thoughts, philosophies, and emotional states — all of which are components of my consciousness.

Foods, atmospheric conditions, accidents and all manner of things also affect the quality of my health. How differently would the effect of these experiences be in my life if I lived in harmony with my intuitive input?

If the fabric of my being is flexible and responsive to intuitive input, then my diet might change, the people I draw into my life might be different, even where I go can change in positive ways. My immune system can also improve and enable greater overall health.

The pathway of our evolution is neither clear nor straight. There is much that needs to be understood. The energy patterns of my aura have layers and relationships that I don't see. Life is an adventure. This adventure has as its goal personal evolution. Quality changes yield quality results. When these results are experienced, life is enhanced.

This journey called life is a paradox of mystical dimensions, and patience is essential. All of the spiritual virtues, when lived, bring a deep well of compassion that can ease the journey. The emotional and mental dimensions weave together with spiritual essence to bind all energy patterns into physical form. Aware consciousness empowers us in this grand adventure.

During an evening walk with a friend, he pointed out the light emanating from Mars. The night sky was brilliant, beautiful. The Milky Way was clear. I could feel our position in the flow of The Milky Way and sense the vast amount of chi that composes our universe. The recognition and feeling that all that energy is present and available to help us create who we choose to be is a full and profound experience.

Gazing at the night sky, I breathed the fantastic energy through my being and throughout the universe - energy to be, to create, and to evolve.

=

15.
Potential

My friend Peter and I were traveling on an unfamiliar road edged with thick, deep woods in New Brunswick, Canada during the spring of 1991. The morning air was bright and clear. We were transporting a sacred object to the Atlantic Ocean in order to conclude a spiritual ceremony that we had been involved in for the past two weeks with the Native People of Eastern Canada.

Both of us felt unsure of the road we were on. We were losing our confidence. We exchanged a look that signaled our mutual concern that we had lost our way. Immediately a hawk flew out of the woods from the right side. It happened so suddenly, it seemed as if a bit of tree had taken form and streaked through the air into our lives. The hawk flew ahead of the car, taking a position just over the front of the hood. Peter was driving at 40 miles per hour.

The hawk was a mature bird with brown feathers, a reddish tail, and a powerful presence. The hawk turned its head looking over its right wing directly into my eyes. I was in disbelief at how it could contort its body while flying along with us. Time and our concerns ceased to exist. The hawk held my attention until I understood its determination to give us clarity about where we were. Then the hawk returned its focus to the road.

Peter and I looked at each other with astonishment as I said, "We're going in the right direction!" As soon as I made that statement, the hawk flew off, gone as suddenly as it appeared. We felt a powerful confidence. The remainder of the ride to the coast was like floating on a cloud. Soon we breathed the briny sea air and enjoyed the sound of the surf.

In ritual we arranged the wooden gate that had been imbued with sacred energy from the long ceremony. Filled with the intention that this sacred object continue to spread the energy of enhancing community health and happiness, Peter set the wooden talisman into the ocean. We sang a song of celebration as we watched the tide float the sacred object out to sea.

Such events continue to be a part of my growth in understanding the potential fullness of life. Developing the awareness that there is more going on in life than originally imagined has been a profound and rewarding process.

Like the hawk above, I am now responding to a felt responsibility to share my journey. We humans are expansive beings with potential far beyond the fears and confusion that can be part of our everyday lives. Security in life is our right. Understanding how our emotions, desires, disappointments, and joys contribute to our health and security is essential. Health and healing involves our entire being.

The adventure of life takes us through highs and lows. Our body, mind, emotions and spirit integrate together to form the fullness of our experiences. We can build on the expansive potential we feel during times of happiness using awareness and intention.

Dramatic life changes like war, injuries, divorce and death are difficult. They show our basic expectations of life to be illusions. Replacing those illusions with qualities of virtue that help us realize our true potential requires that we live with conscious awareness.

Making personal changes that can ease and eventually eliminate pain confirm the powerful relationship that we have with our own fabric of health — how we relate to our body, mind, emotions and spirit can change our lives. The potential for healing, and growth in character, is always present. In this way, health issues can be seen as an opportunity: an opportunity to understand the limitations that disharmonious energy has created within us, and to begin the process of reaching the potential of the person we know ourselves to be.

≡